George Henslow

The Origin of Plant Structures

by Self-Adaptation to the Enviornment

George Henslow

The Origin of Plant Structures
by Self-Adaptation to the Enviornment

ISBN/EAN: 9783337973667

Printed in Europe, USA, Canada, Australia, Japan

Cover: Foto ©berggeist007 / pixelio.de

More available books at **www.hansebooks.com**

THE ORIGIN

OF

PLANT STRUCTURES

BY SELF-ADAPTATION TO THE ENVIRONMENT

BY THE

REV. GEORGE HENSLOW

M.A., F.L.S., F.G.S., Etc.

AUTHOR OF "THE ORIGIN OF FLORAL STRUCTURES," ETC. ETC.

"The end of our foundation is the knowledge of causes and secret motions of things."—BACON.

"What determines molecular motion ! The fundamental problem of Nature."—CROLL.

"The direct action of the medium was the primordial factor of organic evolution."—SPENCER.

PREFACE

In my former work, "The Origin of Floral Structures through Insect and other Agencies,"[1] I endeavoured to prove that the direct action of the environment, in its widest sense, coupled with the responsive power of protoplasm, in other words, the two well-recognised factors of Evolution, are the sole and efficient causes of adaptive variations in plants.

They have nothing to do with Natural Selection, the latter being, as Darwin says, "a totally distinct consideration."[2]

Since, however, variations of structure are the sources of varieties of plants, and varieties are simply incipient species, it is clear that if the environment can be proved to be a perfectly efficient agent in stimulating the inherent variability of plants, the question at once arises, What, if any, aid does Natural Selection supply in the Origin of Species?

The answer to this depends upon another question, viz., Does the environment induce indiscriminate, or, as Darwin calls them, "indefinite" variations? Such would be necessary for the Darwinian hypothesis, which erroneously assumes

[1] International Scientific Series, vol. lxiv., 1888.
[2] Animals and Plants under Domestication, vol. ii. p. 272.

that plants, when they vary, do so indefinitely in nature,[1] and that the environment then (metaphorically) "selects" the best fitted to survive.

My reply is that a new environment does not, in any sense of the term, "select" at all; but *itself induces a plant to form definite*, and not indefinite variations in nature.

Lastly, definite variations are *always* in the direction of adaptation to the environment itself.

If this be so, then, as Darwin assures us, Natural Selection is not wanted at all, so far, at least, as the Origin of Species is concerned.[2]

The object of the present work is to substantiate these statements, and thereby to maintain the same view as to the origin of vegetative structures which I have advocated in my former work for that of floral structures; so that the two books taken together, it is hoped, will furnish a tolerably complete proof of the truth that the origin of all plant structures issues from self-adaptation to the environment (directly or indirectly), without the aid of Natural Selection.

I will now present in a concise epitome the object in view, viz., to prove that the Origin of Species in plants is solely due to the direct action of the environment; and to show that it is one which Darwin fully recognised as

---

[1] "Indefinite variability is a much more common result of changed conditions than definite variability."—*Origin of Species*, 6th ed., p. 6. This was Darwin's fundamental mistake; for definite variation is a law of nature. See *infra*, p. 26.

[2] Animals and Plants under Domestication, ii. p. 271.

existing, but with the reservation that he thought it to be exceptional, instead of its being the rule in nature. This epitome will be more fully expanded in the First and Introductory Chapter.

I. Darwin asserts that Natural Selection has no relation whatever to the primary cause of any modification of structure.[1]

II. A changed environment—especially that of cultivation—stimulates variability, *i.e.*, the innate capacity of varying, which results in variations of structure. This fact is recognised by Darwin, Weismann, Spencer, and all other biologists.

III. Under cultivation, variations, especially after several years, are often indefinite, as may be seen in wheat, maize, and in numerous garden plants (but not in all, as sea-kale and asparagus). Hence artificial selection is absolutely necessary.

IV. In nature, variations are *always* definite, and not exceptionally so, as Darwin thought. The consequence is that "all or nearly all the individuals become modified in the same way."[2]

V. The result of the proceeding is that a new variety, and thence a new species, would be produced "without the aid of Natural Selection."[3]

---

[1] Animals and Plants under Domestication, vol. ii. p. 272. *Cf.* pp. 250, 253, 256, 257.

[2] Origin of Species, 6th ed., p. 106.

[3] Animals and Plants under Domestication, vol. ii. p. 271

Had Darwin studied plants in a state of nature to the same extent as cultivated ones, he would soon have discovered that this last-mentioned result of the direct action of the environment is the rule, and not the exception. The consequence, however, will be seen to be of vital importance to his theory; because, having started with the wrong assumption, that variations were indefinite in nature, just as they so often are under cultivation, he was obliged to call in the imaginary aid of Natural Selection to correspond with the artificial aid of man under cultivation.[1]

The truth, therefore, which I propose to establish is precisely that which Mr. Herbert Spencer has stated in the following words:—"Under new conditions the organism immediately begins to undergo certain changes in structure fitting it for its new conditions;" to which I would only add, that its offspring all alike carry on those changes till equilibrium is established between them and the external conditions of the environment.

It is interesting to find that, though science was in a somewhat elementary condition in his day, Bacon was impressed with the truth of Evolution or the transmutation of species, though partly in a wrong sense, on much the same grounds as those which I shall advance in the present work; and he also advocates experiments to test it. As my readers

[1] In a correspondence with the late Professor Romanes last spring on this subject, he wrote me as follows:—"Of course, if you could prove that indiscriminate [i.e., indefinite] variations have not occurred in wild plants, but only under cultivation, you would destroy Darwinism *in toto*." (Hyères, March 12, 1894.)

may not all know what he has said on the subject, I will conclude this preface with a quotation from his writings.

"Experiments in consort touching the degenerating of plants, and of the transmutation of them one into another. Century VI.

518. "The rule is certain, that plants for want of culture *degenerate to be baser in the same kind;* and sometimes so far as to change into another kind.

1. "The standing long, and not being removed, maketh them degenerate.

2. "Drought, unless the earth of itself be moist, doth the like.[1]

3. "So doth removing into worse earth, or forbearing to compost the earth (as we see that water-mint turneth into field-mint, and *the colewort into rape, by neglect,* &c.).

526. "You must make account, that if you will have one plant change into another, you must have the nourishment overrule the seed; and therefore you are to practise it by nourishment as contrary as may be to the nature of the herb, so nevertheless as the herb may grow; and likewise with seeds that are of the weakest sort, and have least vigour.

"You shall do well, therefore, to take marsh-herbs, and *plant them upon tops of hills* and champaigns, and such plants as require much moisture, upon sandy and very dry grounds. As, for example, marsh-mallows and sedge upon

---

[1] Illustrated below, chaps. ii., iii., and ix.

hills, cucumber and lettuce seeds and coleworts upon a sandy
plot; so, contrariwise, plant bushes, heath, ling, brakes, upon
a wet and marshy ground.[1] This I conceive also, that all
esculent and garden herbs set upon the tops of hills will
prove more medicinal,[2] though less esculent, than they were
before. And it may be likewise some wild herbs you may
make sallad herbs. This is the first rule for transmutation
of plants."

To these acute observations of Bacon I would add the
following remarks on the passages I have italicised :—

518. This view is now maintained by botanists ; though since
Bacon's time it has been asserted that cultivated plants degenerate
into their wild and original forms. They, however, as Sir J.
D. Hooker maintains,[3] are, as in Bacon's words, "baser" forms
of the same kind.

3. Similarly Sir J. D. Hooker remarks that *Brassica campestris,*
var. *oleifera,* "may be a starved state of the turnip escaped from
cultivation."[4]

526. The experiments here suggested are just those which MM.
Bonnier and Flahoult have carried out with plants of low altitudes and latitudes, by growing them in higher ones.[5]

---

[1] See below, chap. ii., for experiments with *Ononis spinosa.*

[2] Pliny noted this fact, which agrees with nature ; vegetable products
as resins, balsams, &c., are correlated with a dry atmosphere. See *infra*
chaps. iv. and v.

[3] Introduction to Flora of Tasmania, pp. viii. ix.

[4] Student's *Flora of the British Isles,* p. 32.

[5] Referred to below in the chapter on Alpine and Arctic plants.

CONTENTS

THE ORIGIN OF PLANT STRUCTURES

CHAPTER I

INTRODUCTORY: ON THE ORIGIN OF SPECIES WITHOUT THE AID OF NATURAL SELECTION

NATURAL SELECTION PLAYS NO PART IN THE ORIGIN OF SPECIES. —I will now develop more fully the points emphasised in the epitome of my subject given in the preface. The purport, then, of this book is, I repeat, to prove that the origin of species issues out of the direct action of the environment, through the responsiveness of protoplasm in the organism itself; and as we are all so familiar with the title of Darwin's work, "The Origin of Species by means of Natural Selection," it is important to insist upon the fact that their real origin has nothing to do with natural selection itself at all. Darwin himself enforces this upon his readers, saying that the primary causes of the origin of variations of structure—which are, of course, themselves the sources of the origin of specific characters—are quite independent of natural selection.

His words are as follows :—"The direct action of the conditions of life, whether leading to definite or indefinite results, is a totally distinct consideration from the effects of natural selection ; for natural selection depends on the survival under

A

various and complex circumstances of the best-fitted individuals, but has no relation whatever to the primary cause of any modification of structure." [1]

Similarly with regard to cultivated plants and domesticated animals he says:—"If we ask ourselves why this or that character has been modified under domestication, we are, in most cases, lost in utter darkness. Many naturalists, especially of the French school, attribute every modification to the 'monde ambiant,' that is, to a changed climate, with all its diversity of heat and cold, dampness and dryness, light and electricity, to the nature of the soil, and to varied kinds and amount of food. By the term definite action, I mean an action of such a nature that, when many individuals of the same variety are exposed during several generations to any change in their physical conditions of life, all, or nearly all the individuals are modified in the same manner. A new sub-variety would thus be produced without the aid of natural selection." [2]

The latest writer advancing these views is Professor Eug. Warming in a paper describing the vegetation of Lagoa Santa in Brazil,[3] in which, after alluding to the many features characteristic of that dry region, he observes :—"Il y a lieu de penser que ces adaptations se produisent directement sous

---

[1] Animals and Plants under Domestication, vol. ii. p. 272.

[2] *Ibid.*, p. 271.

[3] *Lagoa Santa* (Brésil), *Etude de Géographie Botanique; Rev. Gén. de Bot.*, v. p. 144, 1893. The above quotation is abundantly illustrated and enforced by the author in the work itself, entitled *Lagoa Santa: Et Bidrag tel den biologiske Plantegeografi, af Eug. Warming* (Copenhagen, 1892). Having sent him a copy of my "reply" to Mr. Wallace, entitled "The Origin of Species without the Aid of Natural Selection" (*Natural Science*, vol. v. p. 257), he writes me as follows :—"I am altogether in accordance with your views, as you will have seen from *Lagoa Santa*" (Copenhagen, January 14, 1893).

l'influence du milieu, et qu'il n'est pas besoin, pour les expliquer, d'invoquer les lenteurs de la sélection naturelle.
Tout au moins le milieu physique peut agir directement
pour développer les épines, pour diminuer la dimension des
feuilles, &c. Ces modifications, directement déterminées par
le milieu, seraient fixées par la succession de milliers de
générations."

I would here add, that in 1851 Mr. Wallace observed that
local varieties of butterflies and other groups of insects " seem
to indicate that climate and other physical causes have, in
some cases, a very powerful effect in modifying specific form
and colour, and thus directly aid in producing the endless
variety of nature." [1] Similarly, eighteen years afterwards, Dr.
Weismann came to precisely the same conclusion, for he says :
—" It must be admitted that there are cases, such as the
climatic varieties of certain butterflies, which raise some difficulties against this explanation [direct influences upon the
germ-cells]. I myself, some years ago, experimentally investigated one such case, and even now I cannot explain the facts
otherwise than by supposing the passive acquisition of characters produced by the direct influence of climate." [2]

M. Ed. Heckel takes the same view, for he observes, when
discussing the origin of the bright colours of Alpine flowers :—
" Je veux me rappeler seulement que le végétal est dans son
ensemble le résultat du plexus des forces ambiantes qui l'en-
tourent, qui l'enlacent, et qui lui impriment son cachet morpho-
logique en s'alliant aux premières impressions plastiques données
par l'hérédité." [3]

Lastly, Dr. St. G. Mivart says :—" It seems, then, to be
undeniable that the characters and the variation of species are

---

[1] On Natural Selection, p. 179.
[2] Essays upon Heredity, &c., Eng. ed., p. 99.
[3] *Bull. de la Soc. Bot. de Fr.*, 1883, p. 149.

due to the combined action of internal and external agencies
acting in a direct, positive, and constructive manner."[1]

THE SUPPOSED REQUIREMENTS OF NATURAL SELECTION.—I
may say, at once, that the conclusions arrived at by these
and other writers are precisely what I shall endeavour to
prove to be correct both from observation and experiment;
though, as soon as a large number of seedlings put in an appearance, natural selection at once steps in, so to say, with the
result that all those with too weak a *constitution* to maintain
themselves fail to withstand the struggle for existence and to
come to maturity, the stronger plants only proving themselves
the best fitted to survive. This process of selection, however,
is quite independent of any modifications in morphological
structure, by which " varieties " or " sub-species," &c., are alone
recognised.

I would strongly emphasise this fact; for when one speaks
of "the survival of the fittest" out of the superabundance of
offspring which are born—the average number of those which
survive remaining constant—Darwinians assume that this survival turns upon *structural differences*, arising from "the law
of variation," which Mr. Wallace describes as follows:—"Offspring resemble their parents very much, but not wholly—each
being possesses its individuality. This ' variation ' itself varies
in amount, but it is always present, not only in the whole being,
but in every part of every being. Every organ, every character, every feeling is individual; that is to say, *varies* from
the same organ, character, or feeling in every other individual."[2]

Now, I would ask any Darwinian if there is any evidence,
direct or indirect, that any such trivial morphological differ-

[1] On the Development of the Individual and the Species, &c. *Proc.
Zool. Soc.*, June 17, 1884, p. 472.
[2] On Natural Selection, p. 266; *cf.* Origin of Species, p. 34.

ences as are here alluded to are of the slightest consequence to a *seedling*, so as to enable it to survive in the struggle for life, and what attempts have been made experimentally to test the truth or the reverse of this hypothesis?

Let it not be forgotten, too, that specific and generic characters are more often taken from the flowers and fruits, organs which are totally undeveloped when the destruction among germinating plants takes place; and therefore they must be all put out of court so far as natural selection is concerned in bringing about the survival of the fittest.

It has been suggested that a plant survives because, say, of some superiority in the structure of the flower, this feature being correlated with a more vigorous constitution than that of other seedlings, which die in a premature state. I reply that this simply begs the question, or is "putting the cart before the horse." *A seedling survives among others solely because it is vigorous.* This is capable of proof. And whatever flowers it may subsequently bear, it must be contented with them, whether they be the "best" or not for pollination by insects or otherwise.

Moreover, in this definition, Mr. Wallace has omitted to state that morphological variations of any importance, as a rule, only arise in plants when the environment is changed. As long as a wild species is living, generation after generation, in precisely the same conditions, there are no such pronounced variations as are capable of giving rise to a new sub-variety. Nevertheless, the average number of plants is maintained, first, because thousands of seeds never germinate at all; and secondly, of those which do, a vast number perish because they are too poorly nourished, and are soon crowded out of existence, to say nothing of the ill-luck of all that fall on stony ground, &c., or are devoured by animals. In corroboration of this statement, I would refer to my own experiments with small and large seeds selected from average batches of different kinds. They proved that the larger and better nourished have a much greater facility in starting, and soon crowd upon the rest by growing more quickly into larger plants. Conversely, if small seeds be selected for some years, the plants either die out altogether by failing to produce seed, or a tiny race of beings is for a time maintained.

Mr. B. J. Galloway has similarly experimented with radish seed. He finds that large seeds will mature their crop faster. and more evenly than small seeds ; 80 per cent. of the total crop maturing at the same time. The average that can be gathered from a crop from small seeds is only 50 per cent. In point of repeated crops or successive returns from the same ground, large seeds produce five crops, while small seeds produce four.[1]

DARWIN'S FUNDAMENTAL ERROR.—I think it cannot be doubted that Darwin was more than injudiciously hampered by limiting himself to observations upon domesticated animals and plants ; and that, as a consequence, he founded his theory of the origin of species by means of natural selection in nature on a false analogy, based on the artificial selection of cultivated plants and domesticated animals, among which, indeed, Dr. Weismann says[2] that natural selection does not occur at all.

Mr. Wallace drew attention in his original paper on Natural Selection to the profound differences that obtain between domesticated animals and wild ones, concluding his comparison with the following remarkable words :—"We see, then, that no inferences as to varieties in a state of nature can be deduced from the observation of those occurring among domestic animals. The two are so much opposed to each other

---

[1] *New Science Review*, No. 2. vol. i. p. 230.
[2] *Essays on Heredity, &c.*, 1889 (On Panmixia), p. 90.

in every circumstance of their existence, that what applies to the one is almost sure not to apply to the other."[1]

Mr. Wallace was not alone in this opinion, for M. Pouchet insisted that variation under domestication throws no light upon the natural modification of species. Mr. Darwin says that he " cannot perceive the force of his arguments, or, to speak more accurately, of his assertions to this effect."[2]

This divergence of opinion from Darwin has not, I think, been hitherto sufficiently noticed or emphasised.[3] Nevertheless, Mr. Wallace still advocates Darwinism, i.e., he believes in the origin of species by means of natural selection acting on hypothetical variations of structure, which are erroneously supposed to occur *indefinitely in nature*, though he may differ from Darwin as to the amount of support cultivation may furnish to the theory.

Curiously enough, as it seems, at least to me, to be the case, it is under cultivation that the very conditions supposed to be necessary for natural selection are best furnished : for the two chief requirements, or at least the best for natural selection, according to Darwin, are a number of individuals of the very same kind, and all of them growing thickly together.[4]

Now cultivation would seem to illustrate this remarkably well ; for a farmer, for example, in raising a crop, first cleans

[1] *Journ. Linn. Soc.*, 1858, p. 61.

[2] Introduction to Animals and Plants under Domestication, vol. i. note, p. 2.

[3] It is alluded to by Sir J. D. Hooker. Introd. Essay to the Flora of Tasmania, p. vii., note.

[4] This was the condition supplied by Darwin in his experiments described in " The Cross and Self-Fertilisation of Plants," and it is almost the only kind of struggle he will admit, as far as the origin of species is concerned. He does not seem to provide for plants growing in an uncongenial physical environment, but not necessarily crowded, as in the " wadys " or dry water-channels of the deserts, to which reference will hereafter be made.

the seed so as to get an unmixed quantity of the same sort.
A certain space of ground is prepared and sown with the one
kind alone.   They come up more or less thickly, their roots
intertwining within the same limited area, as, *e.g.*, in a field of
clover, so that they are practically struggling for existence
together.   Hence these artificial conditions are just those
which are supposed to be most favourable for the action of
natural selection.

Indeed, Darwin has described an interesting case which
occurred in his own garden.   He grew some beds of *Mimulus
luteus* for seven generations.   In the fourth self-fertilised
generation a white variety arose which was highly self-fertile,
and so numerous in its offspring that it completely excluded
the parental form, to such an extent as to render the experiments no longer really trustworthy.[1]

The fact is, that the artificially prepared medium of a garden
or a field is only one out of a multitude of environments ; and
when seeds are sown in a garden, or wild plants transferred
to it, they *at first* respond to their new surroundings in a
perfectly *definite* and analogous way to their behaviour in
water, deserts, arctic and alpine regions, or any other kind of
district in nature.   It is only . *after prolonged cultivation*, as a
rule, that *indefinite* variations follow.

Let us now pass on to the case in which plants are not
crowded, but grow in an uncongenial environment in nature.
This is a condition which Darwin, as I have observed, has not
sufficiently considered.   He bases his theory of Natural Selection on *the struggle between living organisms*, and to a much
less degree on the environment.   My contention is, that precisely the reverse really obtains ; that morphological adaptations arise, and are maintained—not in consequence of any

---

[1] Cross and Self-Fertilisation of Plants, p. 67.

struggle with other living beings of the same or of different species—but solely through the direct action of the new environment. The following are Darwin's words :—" If a number of species, after having long competed with each other in their old home, were to migrate in a body into a new and afterwards isolated country, *they would be little liable to modification ;* for neither migration nor isolation in themselves effect anything. These principles [*sic*] come into play only by *bringing organisms into new relations with each other,* and in a *lesser degree* with the surrounding physical conditions." [1]

In support of my contention I will take the case of the plants of the deserts around Cairo. There are plenty of individuals in certain places, but they never grow crowded. They only exist on the dry beds called " wadys " or lines of watercourses, but they are always dotted about, never forming large masses, nor are there any areas containing a mixture of plants, as by our own roadsides, &c. There is absolutely no struggle at all with each other; but the struggle is all against the physical difficulties of soil and climate, and it is intense ; the whole structure of their anatomy being in strict adaptation to meet the difficulties of their existence.

In this latter case, therefore, natural selection, according to Darwin, can have no place at all.

The question, however, resolves itself into this : which probability or hypothesis do *the facts* of the case seem to favour most, viz., that *indefinite* variations arise from some assumed internal causes, of which variations only those in harmony with the environment survive, and are. said, therefore, metaphorically, to be selected by it ; or is it that the external forces of the environment excite the variability which is inherent in plants, and call into action the responsive power of the

[1] Origin of Species, p. 319 (the italics are mine); but *cf. infra,* pp. 18–20.

protoplasm in the various species of plants, which thus *all* tend to put on the same or similar, or at least adaptive and *definite* variations of one sort or another, so that there are *no* indiscriminate and wasted variations at all! I know an abundance of facts which support the latter contention, but none whatever in illustration of the former hypothesis.[1] Moreover, experimental evidence can in several cases be brought to bear to test the former, but no experiment that I can conceive can prove the truth of the latter; simply because it is impossible to prove that the hypothetical internal and spontaneous causes of variation are not *themselves* indirectly due to this very responsiveness of protoplasm having been previously called into action by the environment.

Now, had Darwin noted more widely how rapidly many wild plants will change in various ways when placed in new conditions, he could scarcely have failed to see that the influences of a new environment are not merely occasional, exceptional, and slight, but that they are of well-nigh universal application, and often profoundly modify the histological, and thence the morphological, and consequently specific characters of plants.

THE REAL LIMITATIONS OF NATURAL SELECTION.—What natural selection really effects seems to me to be practically limited to three things, or even two—the first and third.

First, the limitation of the number of individuals of one and the same individual kind or variety which comes to maturity.

---

[1] Mr. Wallace observes in his paper entitled "The Rev. George Henslow on Natural Selection," in *Natural Science*, September 1894:—"It is of course admitted that direct proof of the action of Natural Selection is at present *wanting*." In my "Reply" (*Natural Science*, October 1894) I asked:—"If it exist, why is it still wanting? Has not one of the many biologists who have studied nature all over the world during the last five-and-thirty years been able to find one single proof?" *

In other words, the majority of offspring always perish in infancy. This I would call "Constitutional" selection.[1]

Secondly, the "delimitation"[2] of varieties and species, *i.e.*, when intermediate forms die out and varietal and specific forms become isolated. The reason why any parental type-form disappears, or, to speak more accurately, is not reproduced, when varieties arise, as on "the confines of the geographical area which a species inhabits, where the best-marked varieties occur,"[3] is because *the new environment compels all the offspring to change in adaptation to itself;* or, as Darwin expresses it, "All or nearly all the individuals are modified in the same manner. A new sub-variety would be produced without the aid of Natural Selection."[4]. Allowing for "survivals," the type-form is, therefore, no longer produced, as its offspring are continually advancing year after year, until a fresh perfect "equilibrial" adaptation to the new environment has been secured. Hence no more individuals of the older type or of the incipient varieties (*i.e.*, intermediate forms of various degrees) are produced. The last and most perfectly adapted variety having become stable, is then, as a rule, the only one which survives and maintains its morphological characters by heredity.

Thirdly, there is the distribution of species in consequence

[1] Darwin frequently alludes to the importance of the "constitution" of plants as an element in their selection. See "Origin," &c., 6th ed., pp. 7, 9, 73, &c.

[2] This is the function of Natural Selection which Sir J. D. Hooker recognises. His words are:—"Of these speculations by far the most important and philosophical is that of the delimitation of species by natural selection, for which we are indebted to two wholly independent and original thinkers, Mr. Darwin and Mr. Wallace" (*Journ. Linn. Soc. Zool.*, vol. iii. p. 45). Introductory Essay to the Flora of Tasmania, p. xi.

[3] Hooker, *op. cit.*, p. v.

[4] Animals and Plants under Domestication, vol. ii. p. 271.

of some dying out from local causes, while others survive them in any given area or period. Similarly of any new arrivals, while some can establish themselves, others may fail to do so. Such might be called the "Distributional" selection of "survivals."

This form of natural selection finds illustrations everywhere; though one cannot always say why any particular species is abundant in one place and not in another. As an example, the following notes have been supplied to me by Rev. Went-. worth Webster from the South of France. He writes :—"I cannot at all make out the *differentia* of soil and position which determine the very restricted and sporadic (so to say) habitat of the *Daphne* round Biarritz and in the Bidasoa valley, nor why the *Anemone fulgens* grows in some spots and not in others. I believe that I know the general conditions in which one may expect to find it, and where it is found if anywhere; but I cannot explain its *absence* when all the requisite conditions appear continually : but this anemone is sporadic only. The Gromwell clings along the coast, and I know almost to a yard where it ends on the red sandstone at an elevation of some 400 metres in this direction ; but soil and geological formation within those limits of its habitat seem to have [no?] effect on it. The *Narcissi* are still more baffling; nor can I see that either size or colour depend on elevation. The *Hepatica* stops at the limit of the tidal wave, and is almost, as far as I can see, confined to calcareous formations."[1]

---

[1] For further discussions on this subject the reader may be referred to *Influence chimique du Sol sur la Végétation des Sommets des Alpes*, par M. J. Vallot ; *Bull. de la Soc. Bot. de Fr.*, 33, 1886, p. 25. *Quelques Observations sur les Relations entre la Distribution des Phanérogames et la Nature chimique du Sol*, par M. G. Bonnier ; *Bull. de la Soc. Bot. de Fr.*, 1879, 26, p. 338. And *Quelques Mots sur les Causes de la Localisation des Espèces d'une Région*, par M. Battandier ; *Bull. de la Soc. Bot. de Fr.*, 1886, 33, p. 189.

REPRESENTATIVE PLANTS AND THEIR ORIGIN.—A special feature in the distribution of plants over the world is what has
been called "representative forms." In allusion to these,
systematic and descriptive botanists make use of such terms as
"ericaceous," "cactaceous," "junceous," &c., or else adopt the
termination " oidal " (like to), as " euphorbioidal," " muscoidal,"
&c., to distinguish the "facies" of certain groups of plants,
not necessarily belonging to the same genus or even order,
which suggests the use of the above and similar terms. Moreover, these terms have often a geographical signification, and
various groups are recognisable as characteristic of definite
areas, such as deserts, marshes, arctic and alpine regions, &c.

Now it has been recognised by authors, as, e.g., Planchon,[1]
that there exists a connection between the exterior resemblance
of many plants and the character of the region where they
grow: in other words, that the identity in character of the
localities and their climates determines a certain conformity of
habit and facies.

Similarly, Linnæus had said in 1763:[2]—"Primo intuiter
distinguit sæpius exercitatus botannicus plantas Africæ, Asiæ,
Americæ, Alpiumque, sed non facile diceret ipse, ex qua nota
nescio quæ facies torva, sicca, obscura, Afris quæ superba,
exaltata Asiaticis; quæ læta, glabra Americanis; quæ coarctata,
indurata, Alpinis."

When one critically examines the plants possessing the same
facies, one finds that it obviously lies in their outward morphology, which is, however, of course correlated with the histological characters of their vegetative system; the reproductive
organs retaining their generic or other characters, by which
their classification is recognised. As well-pronounced examples

[1] *Des Limites de la Concordance entre les Formes, la Structure, les
Affinités des Plantes et leurs Propriétés médicinales.* Montpellier, 1851.
[2] *Philos. Bot.,* 122 (edit. Vienn. Aust. 1763).

of representative plants may be mentioned the fleshy-stemmed Euphorbias and Stapelias, which simulate members of the Cactaceæ; similarly the thick-leaved Aloës of Africa resemble the Agaves of America, while Alpine Veronicas of New Zealand mimic Thujas, and even *Lycopodium*.

Again, the spinescent features of many species are characteristic of dry desert regions. Of these, certain species in one country are represented by other species elsewhere, as in the deserts of North and South Africa, and in Afghanistan, &c.

Conversely, if we select districts of an opposite character, namely, swampy places, we find the "junceous" type often occurring, being represented by plants having the blade of the leaf greatly reduced, as in *Œnanthe fistulosa*, which has its petiole swollen and hollow like those of some rushes.

Representative plants may therefore be regarded as being such as resemble one another in having similar vegetative structures and habits, correlated with similar external physical conditions.

Plants may also resemble one another without being representative. This has often been observed of many parasites in which all green foliage is wanting; a degeneracy of the tissues, and often of the reproductive organs as well, being characteristic features. Again, in insectivorous plants there are certain peculiarities which they have in common. The stems of woody climbers have been recognised as possessing certain similar anomalies, &c.

Now the question arises, what has caused these features which thus give rise to peculiar facies and similar structures respectively? The answer I propose to give is, that they are due to *the responsive power of protoplasm, which, under the influences of the external forces of the environment, builds up just those tissues which are the best fitted to be in harmony with the environment in question.* This at once accounts for the same features appearing in so many different plants, and in a great number of places on the globe; for protoplasm of one and the same kind is the common property of all.

The argument in support of this contention is twofold.

First, that a distinct cause [1] and effect lie between the environment and the adaptation is a generalisation based upon a vast number of coincidences in each case. This is the well-known argument of "accumulated probabilities," which, when they reach the high proportion which nature affords in the present case, amount to a "moral conviction" equivalent to a "demonstration."

Secondly, the additional proof is, with rare exceptions, forthcoming, viz., "the verification by experiment." Beyond these two kinds of proof nothing more is required.

THE WRITER'S AND DARWIN'S VIEW CONTRASTED.—It will not be amiss to state at this point concisely how this line of argument differs from Darwin's. The three factors of the problem are, first, heredity and atavism, or the tendency to reproduce the features of the parental or ancestral types in the offspring; secondly, variability, or the power of changing structures; and thirdly, the environment, or the external conditions of existence. Darwin recognised the fact that besides the obvious "tendency" to reproduce the parent type (heredity),

---

[1] It may be worth while adding here that *veræ causæ* are themselves unknown and unknowable, because we do not understand the nature of life, nor can we give any explanation of the "how" and the "why" its concrete representative, "protoplasm," acts as it does. As there is no use in attempting to explain how protoplasm can build up any organism, animal or vegetable, from the egg to the adult state, so is it equally useless to look for the *vera causa* of its building up one slightly different from the parent, when the seed grows under new environmental conditions. "Self-adaptation," therefore, must not be regarded as "a cause," but only a term descriptive of the objective visible process of change which experiments offer for our study.

there was, *under stimulation*, an equally obvious "tendency" to vary;[1] and, as Professor Huxley writes, "Darwin has shown that—given variation [variability?] and given change of conditions—the inevitable result is the exercise of such an influence upon organisms that one is helped and another impeded [?]; one tends to predominate and another to disappear;"[2] so that "when a variety has arisen, the conditions of existence are such as to exercise an influence which is exactly comparable to that of artificial selection."[3]

It is here assumed by Professor Huxley that of the variations, which are supposed to arise mainly spontaneously or "accidentally," some only are useful, *i.e.*, adaptive; so that for teleology "Darwin substitutes," says Professor Huxley, "the conception of something which may fairly be termed a method of trial and error. Organisms vary incessantly; of these variations the few meet with surrounding conditions which suit them and thrive, the many are unsuited and become extinguished."

There are fundamental objections to the hypothesis as thus stated.

First, variations do not arise accidentally or spontaneously in nature, as long as the same environment is maintained; but since they *do* arise when it is changed, it is at least *à priori* probable that the latter first induces the right variation to appear. Secondly, there is not a strong *à priori* probability that nature, who made no mistakes nor adopted any "trial and error" system in the inorganic world—as in establishing the laws of gravity, light, heat, electricity, &c., and in those of the formation of crystals, chemical combinations, &c.—should be

---

[1] Professor Huxley describes this tendency in "Darwiniana" as "being incessant" (p. 84), but "occasionally" (p. 452).

[2] Darwiniana, p. 103.

[3] *Op. cit.*, p. 433.

so often at fault, and to such an overwhelming extent as the theory requires, in evolving living organisms.

Instead, therefore, of assuming the birth and immediate death of infinite failures in the organic world—of which, too, be it observed, there is no adequate evidence forthcoming—is it not a much more feasible hypothesis that adaptive variations never arise until and unless they are wanted, while badly adapted ones never arise at all except as occasional "monstrosities," which no one would classify as "varieties" in nature?

There would seem to be some confusion between the terms "variability," *i.e.*, a capacity for varying, and a "tendency" to vary. The former is an obvious fact; the latter is disputable. It is worth while considering this a little more in detail.

Recognising variability as an inherent property of plants, since it is obvious that they can and do vary, any innate *tendency* to vary may be questioned, as is, indeed, by Darwin, who says:—"Some authors . . . look at variability as a necessary contingent on reproduction, and as much an aboriginal law as growth or inheritance"[1] . . . "but falsely, as I believe."[2] Thus, some arctic plants (as Dr. Weismann points out) do not seem to have varied since the glacial epoch; and as Sir J. D.

---

[1] Animals and Plants under Domestication, ii. p. 250. Darwin here clearly means by "variability" an *inherent tendency to vary*, so to say, *at all times*. But as I understand the passage, he really agrees altogether with my contention, which I may express in his own words, which follow the above quotation :—"But we must, I think, take a broader view, and conclude that organic beings, *when subjected during several generations to any change whatever in their conditions, tend to vary*" (my italics). There is no necessity, however, for the words "during several generations," as they may begin to change *at once*, though the variations become emphasised and established and then hereditary after "several generations."

[2] *Op. cit.*, p. 253.

Hooker observed : "Some species remain so long hereditarily immutable as to give rise to the doctrine that all are so normally," &c.[1] This, however, is not the same thing as a *capacity for varying*, implied by the word "variability ;" while this power to vary is not called into action until the necessary external conditions are supplied to excite it.

A CHANGED ENVIRONMENT THE CHIEF CAUSE OF VARIATION. —According to some followers of Darwin,[2] new and allied varieties only arise among the offspring of the parent types ; or, in other words, they do not arise in "distant areas," far from that occupied by the type. This, however, is opposed to Darwin's own view, and does not agree with that of Sir J. D. Hooker, than whom there is no more competent judge.

As this is an important matter from the point of view of the origin of species taken by the present writer, it will be as well to quote some few of Darwin's observations. In his chapter on "Variation"[3] he says :—"Among animals which unite for each birth, and are highly locomotive, doubtful forms, ranked by one zoologist as a species, and by another as a variety, can rarely be found within the same country, but are common in separate areas. . .'. Local forms are moderately constant and distinct in each separate island" [of the Malayan Archipelago].

In the following sentence, also, Darwin attributes the origin of varieties to different environments, for he says : [4]—"Alphonse de Candolle and others have shown that plants which have very wide ranges generally present varieties ; and this might

[1] Introductory Essay, Flora of Tasmania, p. viii.

[2] The late Professor Romanes maintained this in his correspondence with me.

[3] Origin of Species, p. 37.

[4] *Ibid.*, p. 43. See also Wallace, On Natural Selection, "Variation as specially influenced by locality," p. 166.

have been expected, as they are exposed to diverse physical conditions. . . . Hence it is the most flourishing, or, as they may be called, the dominant species,—those which range widely are the most diffused in their own country, and are the most numerous in individuals,—which oftenest produce well-marked varieties, or, as I consider them, incipient species."

In other words, there is this correlation : The greater the area, with its greater environmental differences, so much the greater is the number of varieties of a given species.

But Darwin repeatedly says, only varying the expressions :—"Variations of all kinds and degrees are directly or indirectly caused by the conditions of life to which each being, and more especially its ancestors, have been exposed."[1] So also he adds :—"To put the case under another point of view, if it were possible to expose all the individuals of a species during many generations to absolutely uniform conditions of life, there would be no variability" [i.e., variations ?].[2]

Finally he writes :[3]—" Changed conditions of life are of the highest importance in causing variability, both by acting directly on the organisation, and indirectly by affecting the reproductive system."[4]

These quotations will be amply sufficient to show that Darwin's own belief was that varieties did not, as a rule, arise among the offspring of type-species of plants which had grown for long periods in a definite area, but that some changes or other in the environment most readily acquired in nature by

[1] Animals and Plants under Domestication, ii. p. 253 ; cf. pp. 250, 256.
[2] Op. cit., ii. p. 255.
[3] Origin of Species, p. 31.
[4] The reader may also consult the passage " On the Accumulative Action of Changed Conditions of Life." Animals and Plants under Domestication, ii. p. 261.

migration was, as a rule, requisite to stimulate variability or the innate (dormant) capacity for varying.

The reader will observe that in these passages Darwin emphasises somewhat strongly the importance of changed conditions for the production of variations; but in the passages quoted above [1] and in the following he would seem to elevate the nature of the organism to the more important position:—" We clearly see that the nature of the conditions is of subordinate importance in comparison with the nature of the organism in determining each particular form of variation." [2]

Perhaps, after all, neither one nor the other can be regarded as the "more important," but that the response of the organism is precisely equivalent (if not all at once, it will be after some generations) to the action of the conditions. This, at least, would correspond in plants to what Professor Haughton described (if I remember rightly) as the result of "the principle of least action " in animals : that is to say, the development of organ, muscles, bones, &c., is precisely proportional to the forces displayed.

Sir J. D. Hooker, in his "Introductory Essay to the Flora of Tasmania," [3] devoted an article to "The General Phenomena of Variation in the Vegetable Kingdom," and observes :—" As a general rule, the best-marked varieties occur on the confines of the geographical area which a species inhabits."

Again, in speaking of areas characterised by a remarkable uniformity in their phænogamic vegetation, he says that this is associated with "an absence of those varying conditions which we assume to be stimulants to variation in a locality. On the other hand, it is in those tracts that have the most broken surface, varied composition of rocks, excessive climate (within

---

[1] *Supra*, p. 9.   [2] Origin of Species, p. 8.   [3] Page v.

the limits of vegetable endurance), and abundance of light, that the most species are found." [1]

From the preceding quotations it will be gathered that both these eminent and experienced writers attribute stability of form to a permanency of the environmental conditions, and variations of form to changed conditions in the surroundings.

My own experience entirely agrees with these observations of Mr. Darwin and Sir J. D. Hooker. I have carefully examined, e.g., most of the British species of plants which occur in Malta. Not only, as a rule, do they differ in details of structure from the English forms, but some have developed local varieties which differ even from the prevailing Maltese types. Such, however, never occurred intermixed with the common forms.

Thus—to select four examples—Chickweed has four forms: (1) with petals considerably exceeding the calyx (known as *grandiflora*), this has ten stamens; (2) a variety of this last with the petals not exceeding the calyx, also with ten stamens; (3) a similarly small-petaled form, but with three stamens (exceedingly common in England, but rare in Malta); (4) a cleistogamous apetalous form, with (usually) two stamens.

Ranunculus heterophyllus is a form somewhat like *Baudotii*, but not growing in saline water; [2] (2) a form of the same type but with different-sized leaves, &c.; (3) two types of the "trichophyllous" form. None of these grew intermixed. *Capsella Bursa-Pastoris.*—The ordinary very common form is practically the same as in England, but there is a second with

---

[1] Page xiv.

[2] It is an annual in Malta, as it grows in small pools in the rocks, which dry up in summer. I have grown it in England since May 1894. The "floating" leaves at the present time (January 1895) have completely altered their form. From having been wedge-shaped at the base with a crenated anterior margin, they have become deeply lanciniated or palmatifid, with elongated flat and strap-like segments.

"greenish" corymbs, in consequence of the reduction in size of the petals. This occurred in one spot only, as far as I observed, though with many individuals. *Ranunculus Ficaria* is always represented by the form *calthœfolia.*

These few observations, however, are only samples of what may be seen in any special "flora." Thus, Sir J. D. Hooker often, after describing some special variety in "The Student's British Flora," gives its locality as being "maritime," "alpine," "sandy," &c.

Lastly, if we take extreme cases, the question as to one variety issuing from a species in the same environment may be shown to be a *reductio ad absurdum.* Thus, if all species of *Ranunculus* are descended from some one original type, how can the many aquatic forms have arisen by variation *on land,* or, if it be preferred, *vice versâ?*

Again, take the shrubby spinescent species of *Convolvulus* of arid districts, and the climbing species of ordinary soils and climates—what evidence is there of either form having been evolved from the other *under the same conditions in which it grows?*

The preceding illustrations are ample to establish the belief that it is a new environment which excites the variability into action. The plant, having an inherent *capacity* for varying, but no inherent *tendency* to do so spontaneously, responds to the external forces, so that its protoplasm builds up just those tissues which now place the plant and its offspring in a better degree of adaptation to their surroundings than they were in before. This process at once does away with indefinite, as well as all hypothetical and badly adapted variations.

Various authors have speculated as to the nature of protoplasm, proposing to distinguish under that term more than one kind of "plasm" involved in it. It would be quite beyond my province to describe those theories, as they are purely speculative. I therefore prefer to regard the active agent in plants as "protoplasm," and to wait until something more definite can be proved to exist as to any differential characters it may possess, whether of matter or energy.[1]

THE ULTIMATE PROCESS OF VARIATION INSCRUTABLE.—It must not be forgotten, however, that we can never reach the ultimate elements of the problem. The nature and mode of action of life are inscrutable. The question which lies at the bottom of all changes is one which Mr. Croll asked :[2] "What *determines* molecular motion?" He observed that although physical forces are not only interchangeable, but can pass into those which, for want of a better expression, he would call "vital energies ;" yet, as he says, nothing we know of in the properties of physical forces can throw the smallest degree of light upon the above question. There is always, he adds, the "object" which runs through the whole of organised nature ; which cannot be accounted for by means of the known properties of physical forces. In concluding his paper he says :—

"If one plant or animal differs from another, or the parent from the child, it is because in the building up process the determinations of molecular motion were different in the two cases ; and the true and fundamental ground of the difference must be sought for in the cause[3] of the determination of molecular motion. Here, in this region, the doctrine of natural selection and the struggle for existence can afford no

[1] For a refutation of Dr. Weismann's theory of "Germplasm," as far as plants are concerned, the reader is referred to *Natural Science*, vol. i. p. 171.

[2] What Determines Molecular Motion? The Fundamental Problem of Nature. *Phil. Mag.*, July 1872.

[3] It is this "cause" which I regard as the *vera causa* of all structure.

more light on the matter than the fortuitous concourse of atoms and the atomical philosophy of the ancients."

This observation seems to agree with the following remark of Sir J. D. Hooker on the origin of the secretory glands of *Nepenthes*:—" The subsequent differentation of the secretory organs of the pitcher into aqueous, saccharine, and acid would follow *pari passu* with the evolution of the pitcher itself, according to those mysterious laws which result in the correlation of organs and functions throughout the kingdoms of Nature; which, in my apprehension, transcend in wonder and interest those of evolution and the origin of species." [1]

It is the *source* of that "object" of which Mr. Croll speaks, or "purpose," as Darwin called it, or "design," as it used to be styled by the older teleologists, which has baffled all philosophers. It was an easy answer to say that the Great Artificer designed and then created them by a *fiat*. Evolution, however, came to the fore and thrust all antecedent designs aside. But Evolution, after all, has only changed the supposed method of working; it cannot account for the "object," nor for its origin. Mr. Croll's question is still unanswered. Cultivation and experiment clearly prove that plants are *plastic*, and that they can respond to a changed environment; but *how* they can gradually put on structures which, when completed, *look as if they had been designed*, is a question which is as incapable of being answered as the form in which the same problem is asked by Mr. Croll. One thing, however, comes out clearly from the various statements I have gathered together from many observers, as well as from their and my own experiments, namely, that the very outcome of the direct action of the environment is *always* the aggregation of the best possible structures (as far as one can judge) under the circum-

---

[1] Address to the Department of Zoology and Botany of the British Association, Belfast, 1874.

stances, in order to enable the plant to meet the conditions of the environment. Thus the "design" which might be thought to be seen in the forms and colours of flowers, I take to be only the natural and inevitable outcome of the actual visits of insects themselves.

Nothing ever occurs *anticipatory* of an actual adaptation. This was the fundamental error of teleology, and it still lurks beneath any theory of natural selection which requires *anticipatory favourable variations* whereon it may act. The difficulty in accounting for them is not removed if it be thought that such favourable variations arise "fortuitously," or without any connection with the new environmental forces.

SUPPOSED LIMITS OF VARIATION.—That the origin of *some* degree of variation is to be attributed to adaptation in response to the external surroundings of a being is probably admitted by all evolutionists; but such variations are not regarded by many as capable of giving rise to characters which can ultimately become specific; nor as being of equal importance to variations arising from some hypothetical and internal causes, which are assumed to exist, in order to give rise to more pronounced variations; out of the number of which natural selection is said to preserve only such as may prove to be the fittest to survive, and so supply definite characters for the evolution of a new species.

Thus M. Vesque [1] would seem to draw a distinction between *caractères phylétiques* and *adaptations epharmoniques;* but what I would maintain is that the former are only those of the latter kind which have become hereditary, new epharmonic adaptations being continually added as plants readapt

---

[1] *L'Espèce Végétale, Ann. des Sci. Nat.,* 6 Sér. xiii. p. 5, 1881, 6 Sér. xiii. 1882, p. 17; and *Bull. de la Soc. Bot. de Fr.,* 1889, p. 41. See also *Untersuchungen über Variation,* von H. Hoffman, p. 6.

themselves to new environments, thus giving rise to new varieties, species, and genera.

Sir J. D. Hooker makes a somewhat analogous observation :[1]—"Plants that grow in localities marked by sudden extremes of heat and cold are always very variable in stature, habit, and foliage. In a state of nature we say the plants accommodate themselves to these changes, and so they do within certain limits ; but for one that survives of all the seed which germinate in these inhospitable localities, thousands die."

Sir J. D. Hooker uses the expression " within certain limits," but does not say *what* they are nor *why* the thousands of seedlings die.

The answer to the last statement I have already given. With regard to the former, I would venture to describe those " limits " as follows, by saying that the limits of variation in those plants which succeed in adapting themselves to a new environment correspond with the necessary amount of change required, and agree with those recognised by systematic botanists as varieties, and ultimately species, according to the amount of variation necessary to put them into equilibrium with their new surroundings.

In a word, the adaptive variability of plants is itself actually the origin and regulator of all varietal and specific characters, as far as they are deducible from their vegetative system ; just as I have elsewhere shown that the same power is the origin of varietal and specific characters in the reproductive organs of plants.

DEFINITE VARIATION, A NATURAL LAW.—Darwin purposely limited his observations to animals and plants under domestication, as he says :[2]—"It would be travelling beyond my

---

[1] Himalayan Journals. See also Introduction to the Flora of Tasmania, p. 11.

[2] Animals and Plants under Domestication, ii. p. 281.

proper limits here to discuss how far organic beings in a state of nature are definitely modified by changed conditions." He then further observes :—(1) "*It is most difficult to distinguish* between the definite results of changed conditions and the accumulation through natural selection of serviceable variations (2) *which have arisen independently of the nature of the conditions.* If, for instance, a plant had to be modified so as to become fitted to inhabit a humid instead of an arid station, (3) *we have no reason to believe that variations of the right kind would occur more frequently if the parent plant inhabited a station a little more humid than usual.*[1] Whether the station was unusually dry or humid, (4) *variations adapting the plant in a slight degree for directly opposite habits of life would occasionally arise.*"[2]

On this somewhat crucial passage I would offer the following remarks upon the sentences numbered and indicated by italics. (1) The "difficulty" Mr. Darwin felt lies in the fact that while, on the one hand, "the definite results of changed conditions" can be seen and verified by experiments, (as, *e.g.*, by growing spinescent plants in a moist atmosphere, when they become spineless); on the other hand, that an "accumulation through natural selection of serviceable variations" ever exists at all is an *à priori* assumption which cannot be verified, nor proved to have any concrete existence. I would go further, and ask, since the former method is found amply sufficient (as this book will prove) to account for variations of all sorts and degrees, why is it necessary to assume any other unverifiable process?

Moreover, (2) Darwin makes a second assumption that such serviceable variations have arisen independently of the nature of the conditions. How can this be possibly proved? Indeed,

---

[1] But compare this with the quotation (*supra*, p. 19) from "Animals and Plants under Domestication," ii. p. 253.

[2] Animals and Plants under Domestication, ii. p. 290-291.

Dr. Weismann repudiates all sources of variation other than what external conditions give rise to. His words are :—" We are driven to the conclusion that the ultimate origin of hereditary individual differences lies in the direct action of external influences upon the organism." [1]

(3) With regard to the third passage, it seems to me surprising that he should say this, as it is directly contrary to the universal experience of cultivators. The improvements *are* greater and more frequent from parents which have begun to vary themselves from inhabiting the new locality. *Ceteris paribus*, this is equally true for humid stations. (4) The author here states his position clearly, and assumes that suitable variations *would* arise occasionally. This again is a purely *à priori* assumption, for which I venture to say there is not a shadow of foundation in nature. For example, no aquatic plant ever puts forth variations suitable for terrestrial life, *unless its seed be sown on land, or it be transferred bodily to soil out of water.* It may *then*, and often does, grow in adaptation to an aërial and terrestrial existence. Nor does a plant either growing naturally or cultivated in good soil ever produce by seed a plant with the characteristic features of those growing in a desert, *unless the seed be sown in the desert ;* then the seedlings grow up into more or less true " desert plants." Moreover, if a plant be transferred to a new environment, and it grow and leave seed, *all* the offspring feel the same effects of the external conditions and begin to grow in harmony with them. A certain proportion only may survive, but ample to carry on the variations till a new type is established.

Darwin only professed to draw his analogies from animals and plants under domestication. He, however, does appeal to nature in certain instances ; thus he says :—" Although we are

---

[1] Essays on Heredity, &c., Eng. trans., p. 279.

not here concerned with organic beings in a state of nature, I may call attention to one case." He then refers to Mr. Meehan's account of European trees of various orders which underwent changes when grown in America, and adds :—"Hence we are led to infer that they have been definitely caused by the long-continued action of the different climate of the two continents on the trees."[1]

Had Darwin not been determined to limit his observations, but had pursued the subject through nature as he has done under domestication, he would have discovered that this "one case" was but a sample of what is practically *a universal rule.* It is the object of this book to endeavour to fill up this hiatus, and thence to draw a conclusion opposite in character to that of Darwin ; for having gratuitously restricted himself, he was evidently not prepared to foresee how forcible is the argument of adaptation derived from plants in a state of nature.

Darwin in the work referred to then proceeds to say :—"I will give in detail all the facts which I have been able to collect, rendering it probable that climate, food, &c., have acted so definitely and powerfully on the organisation of our domesticated productions, that they have sufficed to form new sub-varieties or races, without the aid of selection by man or of natural selection." The reader must be referred to the detailed account in the work itself,[2] but it may be mentioned here that he gives seven kinds of flowers, three of variegated leaves, about fifteen of vegetable products, four of fruits, three of woods, and five of diseases (which of course have nothing to do with the origin of species). Besides the trees described by Mr. Meehan, he refers especially to maize, which, when transferred from America to Germany, became changed in two or three generations. But in truth there are many cases inci-

[1] Animals and Plants under Domestication, vol. ii. p. 281.
[2] *Ibid.,* p. 272 *seq.*

dentally alluded to in his works which might be added, as,
for example, European sheep when transferred to tropical
countries, as the Indies, lose their wool, the hair becoming
silky in three generations, &c. ·

He observes generally on the above particular instances
mentioned, that "the modifications referred to have been
extremely slight,[1] and in most cases have been caused, as far
as we can judge, by equally slight changes in the conditions."[2]
But can it be safely maintained that such changed conditions,
acting during a long series of generations, would not produce
a marked effect? My reply to this question is that it is precisely the case, and that such is the origin of species.

THE PRESENT ARGUMENT.—I will now proceed to explain
more clearly the line of argument pursued in this book. The
argument for the self-adaptation of plants, as a source of specific
variation, in response to the direct action of the environment,
is based on a very large series of facts. These consist, in the
first place, of innumerable coincidences derived from the study
of morphology and anatomy. They amount to so great an
accumulation of probabilities that the alternative supposition
is, to my mind, unthinkable.

Secondly, it is supported and-established by experimental
evidence or verification. Though the first method of proof is

---

[1] The word "slight" here and elsewhere used by Darwin may mislead;
for it is a general rule that if the same genus of plants is in different
countries, it is represented by totally different species; as, for example, the
Euphorbias (Spurges) in England and the cactus-like forms in Africa; and
if there be the same species growing in wild uncultivated land (and not
merely a weed of cultivation lately introduced), it is usually a variety, and
not absolutely identical with that of the other country; thus a specimen of
Solanum nigrum from the Galapagos Islands in my collection, brought home
by Darwin, has a very minute flower compared with that of rank-growing
plants in English waste ground.

Animals and Plants under Domestication, ii. p. 276.

really and amply sufficient, in the great majority of cases the second can be applied as well, and the evidence is complete and the argument established.

In the preface I alluded to representative plants in anticipation of my determination to take as illustrations plants of deserts and arid districts, alpine and arctic plants, aquatic and amphibious plants, maritime and saline plants, climbing plants, and in addition some miscellaneous structures. Each and all of these will supply series of evidences, so as to say, running parallel with one another, and mutually corroborating the proof derived from each respectively ; so that the argument based upon comparative anatomy will be seen to be cumulative. Direct experimental verification follows in almost every case.

THE CAUSES OF VARIATION TO BE INVESTIGATED.—The fact was, that in arguing on behalf of natural selection, Darwin's attention was not directed to the inquiry into the *causes of variations*, but solely to the selection of some and the destruction of other variations, as are supposed to be the best fitted to survive or the reverse, respectively. Consequently, while natural selection was elevated to a position of importance, the tracing the actual causes or origins of variations themselves was a secondary, or even almost a neglected matter, from his point of view.

Now, however, there is a wide-spread belief, both in Europe and America, that attention should be directed to this previous question, viz., to the discovery of the causes of variations themselves.

Mr. P. Geddes speaks very despondingly on this point, for he says :—" While the fact of the origin of species by evolution is no longer disputed, nor the operation of natural selection upon organic forms any longer denied, the absence of any general theory or rationale of variation in either the animal or the vegetable world is not only generally admitted, but often regarded as inevitable or even hopeless: variation to some writers being simply 'spontaneous' or 'accidental;' to others, if not fortuitous, at least dependent upon causes lying as yet wholly, and perhaps hopelessly, beyond our present powers of analysis." [1]

Similarly the late Professor Romanes wrote so late as 1892 : —"The degree in which variability is indefinite, or on the contrary determinate, is a question which is not yet ripe for decision, nor even, in my opinion, for discussion." [2]

If, however, it can be shown that varietal and specific characters are really attributal to the direct action of the environment, *then*, and not till then, may the further question arise, viz., how far is natural selection required to preserve the best, or, to speak more accurately, to destroy the worst? The conclusion, which appears to me to be inevitable from observations spreading over a very large class of facts, is, that plants do undoubtedly exercise this power of self-adaptation, and that characters thus acquired become in time hereditary, if the conditions of the environment be constant.

I would describe the process, therefore, once more as the result of the responsive power of protoplasm on the one hand, and the forces of the external environment on the other. These two factors I take to be amply sufficient for the whole of the evolution of plant structures, without any aid from natural selection whatever.

[1] On the Nature and Causes of Variation in Plants, *Trans. Bot. Soc. Edin.*, xvi. p. 416.

[2] Darwin and after Darwin, p. 336, *note*.

CHAPTER II

ORIGIN OF THE MORPHOLOGICAL PECULIARITIES OF DESERT PLANTS [1]

INTRODUCTORY OBSERVATIONS.—The general *facies* of the flora of a country with a relatively dry soil and atmosphere is very observable; and when it is found to be the same in widely separated countries, as in the desert regions of North Africa, in the arid districts of North-West India and of Afghanistan, in parts of Australia, in South Africa, in Brazil,[2] &c., so that these several countries afford either the

[1] This and the following chapter have been published in the *Journ. Lin. Soc. Bot.*, vol. xxx. p. 218, 1894.

[2] For an interesting description of the plants growing in a comparatively dry region of Brazil, but of a somewhat less intensity than that of the African deserts, the reader is referred to the paper by M. Eug. Warming referred to above (p. 2). Many peculiarities mentioned by that author correspond more or less exactly with those I have described in this chapter. Grisebach also compares the South African region (Kalahari) with the Soudan :—

"Les autres formes végétales sont les mêmes qu'on retrouve dans d'autres steppes et déserts, ou bien elles signalent l'intime affinité du Kalahari et du Soudan. A la première catégorie appartiennent les plantes grasses (*Euphorbia*, *Mesembrianthemum*), les végétaux bulbeux qui ouvrent rapidement leurs fleurs après les orages d'été (ex. *Amaryllis*); parmi les arbustes, les formes de Spartium (ex. *Lebeckia*), de l'Oléandre (par l'entremise d'une Rubiacée, le *Vangueria*) et du Myrte (par une Ebénacée, l'*Euclea*); enfin, les arbustes à feuilles velues, particulièrement fréquents dans la savane (*Tarchonanthus*)."—*Végétation du Globe*, vol. ii. p. 255-256.

C

same or "representative" plants, one infers (but of course at first merely on *à priori* grounds) that most probably similar causes have produced these similar results. A closer inspection shows that the similarities in the vegetative system of such plants, which often have no affinity between them whatever, can be carried down into the minutest details of histological structure, and that a large proportion of such structures at least are always serviceable to the plants in resisting the deteriorating effects of an insufficient supply of water, as well as of an excess of radiation, and other hindrances to such vigorous growth as is maintained in moister climes.

We thus begin to suspect, indeed very strongly, that the various peculiarities (such, *e.g.*, as the densely hirsute clothing and the consolidation of the mechanical tissues) are the direct results of the dry climatic conditions surrounding the plants, and that the unfavourable environment actually brings about the production of just those kinds of structure which are best able to resist the injurious effects of the climate, and so enables the plant to survive under them. Such, at least, is the result of my own observations on the plants of the Egyptian deserts.

The distribution of similar forms of plants under similar conditions illustrates another fact. We speak of "chalk-loving," "sand-loving," and other kinds of plants frequenting special environments; but these phrases seem to be to a great extent misnomers. Plants by no means all or always "love" the soils alluded to, in which they are often found. Many flourish quite as well, if not better, in a totally different soil. Having, however, been located in them for many generations, they have become so adapted to the peculiar conditions of the soil and climate, *by assuming such structures as are the best under the circumstances*, that they now succeed in them; but at the same time many are always tacitly protesting, so to say, against their environment, for they at once show how much more vigorous they can become when they are grown in a different and more congenial soil.[1]

Similarly we might just as well speak of desert-loving plants, corresponding to the term "Xerophile;" but we know what an intense struggle for existence they have to maintain. Nevertheless they have become so attuned to their difficulties, that when seeds of desert plants are sown in ordinary garden soil they almost invariably fail to grow at all;[2] just as, while some water-plants grow more vigorously on land, others cannot now live if exposed to the air. Or again, with regard to many maritime plants, they will grow just as well, if not better, away from the sea, either by altering their structures, as Samphire does, by developing flat and thin leaves; or else they may retain their usual features, this being due to heredity. Thus *Salsola Kali*, the Prickly Glasswort of our sandy seashores, has become one of the worst weeds ever introduced into American wheat-fields. One year's damage in Dakota alone is estimated at 2,000,000 dollars. It is described as taking complete possession of the soil, whilst its spiny nature makes it objectionable to horses and other animals.[3] In this case the plant has not lost its spines by growing in a richer soil, and illustrates the fact that hereditary influences often, if not always, *tend* more or less to resist the effects of a changed environment: and just as new adaptations can easily become fixed in some cases, but with great difficulty in others, as in cultivating wild plants; so, conversely, while some features

[1] See Battandier's paper, *Quelques Mots sur les Causes de la Localisation des Espèces d'une Région. Bull. de la Soc. Bot. de Fr.*, 1886, p. 189.

[2] This has been the experience of Dr. E. Sickenberger in Cairo, and my own in England. He was good enough to send me a large collection of seeds collected by himself from the deserts; but none germinated, though treated with the greatest care in a hothouse, with the solitary exception of a *Farsetia*, and this soon died.

[3] *Farmer's Bulletin*, No. 10, 1893.

are instantly lost, others are as rigidly retained, though it may
be in a modified form. What, however, may be called the
general "plasticity" of plants is now so well recognised, that
it affords us perfectly adequate means in accounting for the
self-adaptation of plants, although it is far from being necessarily applicable in every feature.

I will now give some special characteristic features of desert
plants, and then compare them with others growing in arid districts, to show the more or less great similarity which prevails.

GENERAL MORPHOLOGICAL CHARACTERS.[1]—On first entering
the desert near Cairo, where plants are to be found, namely,
along the lines of water-courses, which are dry all the year
round excepting in February and March—for no plants occur
on the higher ground at all—the general appearance is of low
bushes or isolated tufts of a nearly uniform grey colour. The
plants are never crowded or cover the ground like an English
roadside. In other words, they do not struggle for an existence
with one another, but only with their inhospitable inorganic
environment.[2] The grey colour is mainly due to intense hairi-

---

[1] The best work I am acquainted with on the structure of desert plants
is one by Dr. G. Volkens, entitled *Die Flora der Ægyptisch-Arabischen
Wüste auf Grundlage anatomisch-physiologischer Forschungen dargestellt ;*
and the Epitome, *Zur Flora der Ægyptisch-Arabischen Wüste, eine vorläu-
fige Skizze.* He gives eighteen plates (4to) illustrative of the anatomy of
a well-selected series of types. I have fortunately been able to collect a
large number of the same plants myself in the deserts around Cairo ; and
for nearly all the rest I am greatly indebted to the kindness of Professor
E. Sickenberger, of the School of Medicine, Cairo : so that I have been
able to examine anatomically nearly the whole series described by Dr.
Volkens, and thus to supplement his observations in some degree in
points he has not recorded. I would also refer the reader to the writings
of M. P. Maury, *Assoc. Franç. pour l'Avancement de Science, Congrès de
Toulouse,* 1887, also *Morot's Journ. de Bot.,* ii. 1888, *Rev. Bibl.,* p. 101.

[2] Similarly of the desert regions of Beluchistan Dr. Aitchison says :—
"The barren character of the country and the want of indigenous trees
is due to the extreme dryness of the soil and aridity of the atmosphere. . . .

ness, which subdues the green hue of chlorophyll. A few plants only, comparatively speaking, have no hair and are consequently greener, as the species of *Zygophyllum*, which are fleshy-leaved plants; but a coating of wax is of frequent occurrence, and this aids in giving a glaucous hue.

The hair and the wax, as well as the fleshy character of the leaves, are all adaptations to arrest the loss of water by transpiration during the summer.

SPINESCENT CHARACTERS.—The next obvious feature is the stunted character of the bushes; three feet high being about the maximum size (*Zilla myagroides*), with gnarled stems at the base. This is often coupled with a spinescent character, either in the branches (*Zilla*), or foliage (*Echinops*), or stipules (*Fagonia*) and bracts (*Centaurea*). These features are, we may say, undoubtedly in the main due to a want of water,[1] which always prevents the formation of cellular tissue, while this deficiency of parenchyma is associated with a hardening of the fibro-vascular, mechanical elements. The converse conditions are witnessed, *e.g.*, in a plant of *Zilla myagroides*, which

The struggle of plant life for existence is great. The plants which are seen to exist through it all are either annuals or those possessing great root-stocks, tubers, tuberous roots, rhizomes, bulbs, or other such structural developments as assist them to baffle and survive through the extremes of temperature."—*A Summary of the Botanical Features of the Country traversed by the Afghan Delimitation Commission during* 1884–85. *Trans. and Proc. Bot. Soc. Edin.*, 1889, p. 426.

[1] So Mr. Belt in "The Naturalist in Nicaragua" says (p. 46) :—"This spiny character of vegetation seems to be characteristic of dry rocky places and tracts of country liable to great drought."

Similarly Grisebach, describing the flora of Kalahari, South Africa, and alluding to spinescent species of Acacia, says :—

"Tous portent des épines qui, chez *A. horrida*, ont 5 à 8 centimètres de longueur. La division limitée du feuillage et l'exiguïté des surfaces sont autant de traits en rapport avec le développement des organes piquants et de la sécheresse du sol."—*La Végét. du Globe*, ii. p. 252. He also alludes to similar features of the Tibetan flora (i. pp. 613, 614).

was the only species, out of many, raised from seed in the Botanic Garden of Cairo by Dr. E. Sickenberger. It not only bore well-developed leaves, but the spines, though formed through the forces of heredity, were very slender and sub-flaccid, instead of being intensely rigid. As an interesting illustration of a highly spinescent plant belonging to the *Cucurbitaceæ*, an order in which it would be least expected, is the Narras plant of Caffraria (*Acanthosicyos horrida*). It grows on the sandy downs on the sea-coast. It has no leaves, but double spines studded all over the branches, forming impenetrable bushes, which spread widely and attain the height of a man. It is curious that although the seeds germinate readily, all attempts to cultivate it in Europe have failed; just as I have failed with many desert plants of Egypt. As examples of other remarkable spinescent plants may be mentioned *Aciphylla squarrosa*, of the order *Umbelliferæ*, described by Sir J. D. Hooker,[1] and *Poterium spinosum* in Palestine.

The hardening of the mechanical tissues generally, which so often results in special spiny processes, is brought about by drought and other conditions of the environment, and is one of the best means for resisting the intense heat of the desert. M. de Candolle[2] calls attention to this fact; he says :—" Very hard wood resists heat because it encloses but little aqueous juices, so there is but little to evaporate." Similarly he remarks upon the great value of cork for resisting both extreme cold as well as extreme dry heat, as there will be a greater number of cells in the layers of cork filled with air, thus making bad conductors between the external air and the cambium layer and alburnum. Thus, old trees resist cold better than young ones. On the other hand, endogenous trees, having no bark, only grow in warm climates. In some, as the Date, the

---

[1] Flora of New Zealand, vol. i. p. 87.
[2] *Essai Elémentaire de Géographie Botanique. Dict. des Sci. Nat.,* vol. xviii.

bases of the leaves, especially if they decompose into a hairy covering, may supply the place of it.

The evidence in support of the assertion that spines are the direct outcome of the environment also rests upon the well-known fact that there are many instances of plants losing their spines altogether when grown under other circumstances. This variableness in the spinescent character of plants is no new observation. Thus G. G. Küchelbecker, in a *Dissertatio Bota-nico-physica de Spinis Plantarum* (A.D. 1756), wrote as follows :—" Sunt autem, quædam plantæ, quæ eundem semper et vbique seruant in extensione superficiei habitum, cum contra ea aliæ, pro varia soli et culturæ indole, formam hanc alias sibi propriam deponant, vel tamen maximam sui partem mutent, ita vt, quæ glabræ antea erant, nunc inæqualitatem magis minusue eminentem induant, atque suum plane deposuisse videantur habitum superficiei pristinum " (pp. 9, 10).

He then refers to Linnæus' *Philos. Bot.*, p. 215, § 272 :— " Spinosæ arbores cultura sæpius deponunt spinas in hortis. . . . Hirsuties loco et ætate facillime deponitur." Again, *l.c.*, p. 247, § 316 :—"Solum mutat plantas, vnde varietates enascuntur, et, mutato eodem, redeunt. Hinc *Acanthi* molles et aculeati ; *Cinaræ* aculeatæ et non aculeatæ."

Similarly at the present day Pears, species of Rose and of *Prunus*, &c., are well known to lose their spines under cultivation.

Grisebach observes generally, with regard to spinescent plants: —" Quand on voit que l'extension géographique des plantes épineuses est en rapport avec la sécheresse du climat, ainsi que cela a été démontré dans une section précédente (tom. i. p. 417), il n'y a plus à se demander si c'est ce fait, ou celui admis par Linné, qui interprète le mieux la signification de tels organes. Il est certain que ce qui caractérise éminemment les opérations de la nature, c'est la tendance à réaliser simultanément, à l'aide des mêmes moyens, les fins vitales les plus diverses ; en sorte que les modifications aussi peu considérables que possible apportées au développement d'un organe, paraissent correspondre tantôt plus à un but qu'à un autre, selon que l'un ou l'autre est favorisé davantage."[1]

Ononis spinosa, L.; has an excessively spiny variety, *horrida*, growing in maritime sands. It is much less spiny in waste places by roadsides, &c., and becomes the variety *inermis* elsewhere. This latter form of the "sub-species" *repens* can be produced, temporarily at least, at will; for when the ordinary spiny form, *O. spinosa*, is grown either in a very rich soil, with an abundance of water, or in a moist atmosphere, whether the plants be raised from cuttings or seeds, they gradually lose their spines. Those first formed under these conditions are much reduced in size and in rigidity. Hereditary influence is too strong to arrest them at first altogether; although none are produced later on vigorous shoots growing in a saturated atmosphere. They reappear as soon as the same plants are allowed to grow in the ordinary way. It may be added that when the spines are arrested, the peculiar odour of *repens* is present, and the flowers also are larger and are like those characteristic of that sub-species.[2]

M. Lotheliet[3] carried out very similar experiments with other spinescent plants. He thus found that by growing *Berberis vulgaris* in a moist atmosphere, it bore no spinescent

---

[1] *La Vég. du Globe,* ii. p. 251–252.

[2] Such were the results of my own experiments in 1891–92. I raised plants from the seeds obtained from these plants in 1893, to see if the hereditary trait of producing spines becomes less pronounced in successive generations. In August the plants had only grown to about five inches in height in consequence of the great drought; but up to the date of writing this (August 15th) they had developed no spines.

[3] *Rev. Gén. de Bot.,* 1890, p. 276; *Bull. de la Soc. de Bot. de Fr.,* 1890, xxxvii. p. 176; *Comptes Rendus,* 1891, cxii. p. 111.

leaves, as the parenchyma was well formed between the ribs and veins, but in a perfectly arid atmosphere it bore spines only. Intensity of light also favoured their production. He found from a microscopical examination that in a section of a spine exposed to moist air the vessels of the xylem are few in number and the pericycle is not lignified. In a dry air the xylem forms a continuous ligneous circle and the pericycle is also lignified. I have myself repeatedly corroborated this observation of the special consolidation of fibrous tissues in several instances in different species of desert plants. This consolidation of the mechanical elements may be perhaps explained as a secondary result of the relative abundance of the assimilative tissues of desert plants; for although the leaves themselves may be very small, their palisade layers are often two, three, or even four in number, and equally developed on both sides of the leaf. While there is a great arrest in area of the parenchymatous tissue—due to the feeble water-supply—the organised products are mainly utilised in the ligni-fication of the supportive tissues.

Conversely, if plants be etiolated by being grown in the dark, while the parenchymatous tissues are relatively in excess, such as the pith and cortex, M. Rauwenhoff has shown that the mechanical tissues are greatly reduced, the assimilative tissues being quite incapable of any activity.[1]

Another instance is supplied by our common water-reed *Phragmites communis.* This grass is very abundant in the Nile Valley, growing in places which are not artificially irri-gated. It covers large areas of waste ground outside Cairo, forming a stunted growth, the leaves being very short and sharp-pointed. It has been named var. *isarica.* Close to the Nile, however, in Rhoda Island, it grows nine or ten feet high,

[1] *Sur les Causes des Formes anormales des Plantes qui croissent dans l'Obscurité. Archives Néerlandaises des Sci. Exac. et Nat.,* xii. p. 297.

with long leaves almost exactly like the plants in English rivers. In many places the two forms of leaf are on the same stem, sometimes even alternating with each other, suggesting the idea that the leaves were elongated, or abbreviated and spinescent, just as the plant happened to have sufficient water at its disposal or not.

In this plant we have, therefore, a varietal character, which is quite inconstant, as it varies repeatedly even on the same stem, and which has not become relatively fixed, though deemed worthy of a name.

Such and other facts show how completely relative many varietal and even specific characters may be. They may have every degree of constancy, but they can often easily change if the environment be altered, till other characters take their place, which may then become relatively fixed in their turn.

I have said that all observations tend to prove that the great reduction of the parenchymatous tissues, and a correlated hardening of the mechanical tissues, so that a spinescent character becomes very characteristic of desert plants, are simply the inevitable results of the action of the environment. That this is so is corroborated by an experiment of M. Duchartre on the effect of drought upon *Dioscorea batatas*.[1]

Some tubers of this plant produced long shoots, but without being allowed to have any water at all. The effect upon the stem was that it acquired excessive rigidity with no heliotropism nor power of climbing. Although the stem was much more slender than normally, there was a marked predominance of the elements of consolidation. The fibres had very thick walls and a minute lumen. The periphery of the central cylinder showed a zone of perceptibly greater thickness than usual, consisting of fibres of small diameter, but with walls of

---

[1] *Bull. de la Soc. Bot. de Fr.*, 1885, p. 156.

greater thickness than usual. This appears to have been the pericycular zone so commonly differentiated in herbaceous endogenous stems. Similarly, the collenchymatous cords at the angles were quite as much developed as in normally grown stems.

Moreover, all these well-developed mechanical elements of consolidation in the *Dioscorea* were in a greater relative proportion, in consequence of the considerable reduction which the parenchymatous tissues had undergone.

The leaves were small and undifferentiated, the parenchyma between the veins being much arrested; the stomata were undeveloped, and the palisade and lax central parenchyma all alike and unformed in character, except that the two of four larger layers in the centre had no chlorophyll.

From the above brief epitome of M. Duchartre's experiment, it will be seen that, so far as the small amount of parenchyma and the great density of the mechanical elements of the fibrovascular tissues are concerned, we have an exact parallel between desert plants and the *Dioscorea* grown without water in the dark. Hence this experiment, together with that referred to above, are sufficient to completely justify the conclusion that the indurated character of the mechanical system, as well as the spinescent features of so many desert plants, are simply the immediate results of the effects of the comparatively waterless character of the environment. Lastly, it must be borne in mind that the spinescent character is hereditary, and although the rigidity begins to break down under cultivation in a moist climate and a good soil, the spines may still be formed, but become gradually modified, and finally disappear, reverting to leafy branches, as has occurred with cultivated Pears and Plums and *Ononis*, or back into leaves in *Berberis*.

That " xerophilous " peculiarities of plants are not only correlated with, but actually caused by the arid conditions of their environment, is also the conclusion of Professor A. F. W. Schimper,[1] who has lately studied the flora of Java. He finds that the plants of the shores, Alpine plants, those of the solfataras, and epiphytes, although very different from each other in a classifactory sense, all present common characters in being strictly "xerophilous." In all, the leaves are small and thick, there is a strong cuticle, the stomata being at the bottom of "crypts," the intercellular spaces reduced, hairs more abundant, the water-storage tissues present, &c. The author concludes from his observations that among the causes capable of determining the development of these various adaptations of defence against a temporary or permanent insufficiency of water, are the dryness of the atmosphere and soil, a strong insolation and rarefaction of the air, the richness of salts, or a too low temperature of the substratum. The stunted condition of the plants of the solfataras and of the shores would be due to the too great abundance of salts in the substratum, which has the result of reducing the assimilation of carbon.

As a corroboration of the preceding it may be added that MM. J. Vesque et Ch. Viet[2] came to the same conclusions, namely, that the fibro-vascular structures were much more developed in a dry than in a moist atmosphere.

I will conclude this section by quoting another corroborative remark of Grisebach :[3]—" Au nombre de phénomènes généralement répandus figure le développement des épines, phénomène qui va en croissant avec la sécheresse du climat. Les arbustes

[1] *Ueber Schutzmittel des Laubes gegen Transpiration, besonders in der Flora Java's* (Mittheilungen aus den Sitzungsberichten der König. preuss. Akademie der Wissenschaften zu Berlin, 1890, Heft vii. 1045). See also *Rev. Gén. de Bot.* for 1892, p. 364.

[2] *De l'Influence du Milieu sur la Structure anatomique des Végétaux. Ann. Sci. Nat. Bot.*, Sér. 6, tom. xii., 1881, p. 167.

[3] *La Végétation du Globe*, ii. p. 197.

épineux plus petits qui habitent les steppes asiatiques et les solitudes du Sahara pénètrent dans les savanes de la contrée basse du Soudan (*Tragacantha, Alhagi*). L'exemple le plus remarquable de ce fait est fourni par le Sider (*Zizyphus spina-Christi*), qui, sous la forme d'un arbuste ou arbre nain, s'étend depuis la Palestine jusqu'au Sennaar et au Bornou. Mais dans le Soudan le développement des épines n'est point limité aux arbustes asiatiques de petite taille, ou à la forme de Sodada, puisque même les arbres, notamment les Acacias, aussi bien que les plantes grasses, sont également armés d'organes piquants. Dans la Nubie la majorité des arbres sont épineux, et il paraît que dans certaines parties de l'Abyssinie et dans le Bornou il n'est presque point de végétal ligneux sans épines. Une chose semblable est rapportée par M. Livingstone relativement aux contrées confinant avec le Kalahari, tandis qu'au contraire cette organisation s'évanouit sur le partage des eaux dans la direction du Congo."

FOLIAGE OF DESERT PLANTS.—Another result of the deficiency of water is the small size of the leaves of desert plants, thereby lessening the surface of the transpiring organs ; or else they are suppressed almost, if not quite, altogether, as in *Retama, Anabasis, Ephedra*, and *Tamarix*. Many plants produce fair-sized leaves in the early spring as soon as the rainy season has arrived, but none or very small ones later on, as *Zilla, Alhagi, Statice*, &c. The inrolled margins of the leaves, which make them assume the form of a more or less closed cylinder, is another common contrivance.[1]

Now while this reduction of surface is beneficial by lessening transpiration, we must remember that it is simply the result of drought. This is proved in several ways: first, one and the same plant will produce much larger leaves in March or April,

[1] Rhododendron leaves temporarily assumed a precisely similar form in the great frost of February 1895.

when a good supply of water is at hand, but minute leaves in June, when the supply is deficient; secondly, if the same plant be grown in the Nile valley, it ceases to produce the smaller summer foliage and resembles the ordinary herbaceous leaves of temperate climates. Thus *Salvia lanigera* growing in the delta has flat leaves eight inches long, but when in the desert they are only about two and a half inches long with the margins inrolled. A similar variability is a common phenomenon and is well known; for numerous instances might be given of leaves varying in form and structure on the same plant, or on different individuals, according as they develop at different times or under different circumstances; or again, if the plant have been transplanted, say, from a hot to a cold, or from a dry to a wet locality; or again, from a low to a high altitude, or *vice versâ*. Mr. Groom records a case of an orchid, *Renanthera albescens*, which naturally scrambles over plants, growing on hot, open, sandy heaths. The specimen was transferred to the Botanic Gardens, Singapore, where it grew under the shade of a well-foliaged tree. As might be expected, the form and anatomical details of the new leaves became much altered. Mr. Groom gives a series of comparisons showing how the cuticle decreased in thickness, while the dimensions of the leaf increased in length, and became diminished in thickness, &c.[1]

Mr. Scott Elliot[2] has independently arrived at a very similar result, as to the cause of the small size of the leaves of the "ericaceous" type which prevails in parts of the Cape and of Australia. He observes:—"The climate (of the Karoo) is characterised by a long and dry summer and by plenty of wind. Such conditions obviously favour transpiration, . . . Hence the small and excessively coriaceous leaves of these plants without

[1] Annals of Botany, vii. p. 152.
[2] Notes on the Regional Distribution of the Cape Flora. *Trans. Bot. Soc. Edin.*, 1891, p. 241.

much spongy parenchyma are thoroughly suited to the climate. We may even, I think, go a step farther, and say that the physical conditions have produced this form. . . . With regard to leaves, certain observations, which are not yet extensive enough for publication, as to the variation in size and texture of the leaf in the same species in different habitats, strongly incline me to believe that the smallness, cuticularisation, and want of spongy parenchyma in the leaf all follow directly from such conditions."

Similarly Professor Eug. Warming attributes a similar result to climate, especially the dryness of the atmosphere on the Campos of Lagoa Santa, Brazil. He writes:—

"Lorsque les feuilles ne sont pas tomenteuses sur les deux faces, elles sont ordinairement raides et coriaces ; les feuilles de plusieurs espèces, agitées par le vent, font entendre un bruit de cliquetis ou de crécelle très extraordinaire, tels sont certains *Salvertia, Vochysia,* le *Palicourea rigida* ou *strepitans* et certains *Bombax.* La majorité des espèces arborescentes ont les feuilles dures et coriaces, à quelque famille qu'elles appartiennent." [1]

These and other features everywhere characteristic of plants growing permanently in arid districts are often noticeable in other plants when only temporarily subjected to great drought. Thus Sign. Bolos writes me from Olot (Genova) about *Rosa sepium.* He says:—"In consequence of a great drought such a transformation took place in a plant of this species that it became unrecognisable. The stalks, leaves, and flowers were reduced to half their size, the stems became much more thorny, the leaves, calyces, and flowers much more glandular."

This illustrates what I shall have more than one occasion to refer to, viz., that it is only a question of degree between an

---

[1] *Op. cit.,* p. 155 (*supra,* p. 2).

accidental and transient effect and a persistent and hereditary one. The difference simply resides in the duration of the climatic influences.

Besides the general reduction in size of the leaves, plants in the desert reach the "subaphyllous" and "aphyllous" conditions. The degradation in the size and form of the leaf passes through many degrees till the leafless stage is reached, as in *Ephedra* and *Retama*. Just short of that, the leaves are minute, scale-like, closely adpressed against the stem, and assume the appearance of the foliage of *Thuja*, *Cupressus*, &c. In the desert this form is well seen in *Anabasis articulata* and *Salsola Pachoi*. Such leaves may terminate in sharp points, as in *Cornulaca macrantha*, just as on our English *Salsola Kali*. This last-named genus adopts both forms, just as *Retinospora* may have them, even on the same plant.

That drought is the main cause is inferred from the fact that similar forms occur on plants in rocky and arid mountain regions at high elevations. Thus while in New Zealand nearly aphyllous species of *Veronica* live at an elevation of 7000 feet, *Veronica Thujioides* is found at a lower but still high elevation. Similarly Thujas (Biotas) are trees and shrubs of considerable elevation. Very many coincidences here offer the same grounds in support of the contention that similar causes have brought about similar results and produced these mimetic and specific forms in genera of widely different orders. Thus *Tamarix* in Africa may be said to "represent" *Haloxylon Ammodendron* of Beluchistan and the Oriental steppes (Aitchison and Grisebach), *Casuarina* of Australia, the Thujas of Japan and California, *Veronica Thujioides* of New Zealand, &c.

SUCCULENT PLANTS.—Although spinescence and hairiness are the prevailing features in the desert plants near Cairo, some few are decidedly succulent, as the species of *Zygophyllum*.

That this feature is one of the direct results of the intense heat (probably influenced by the presence of salts in the soil), inducing the formation of a thick cuticle, which, in turn, involves the retention of water and the development of succulent aquiferous tissues, I think cannot be doubted. The presence of salts has been proved by M. Lesage to be the immediate cause of succulency in maritime plants of temperate climates;[1] and he succeeded in making plants succulent which are not so ordinarily. On the other hand, the structure of "rock plants," such as Sedums, Haworthias,[2] &c., is correlated with their arid and stony surroundings (probably without the aid of salts), and is obviously one of the many adaptations for the storage of water.

That the succulency is due to the direct action of the environment is shown by the results of experiments in which the normal succulency is made to disappear when a new combination of surrounding conditions is supplied to the plant; thus M. Battandier[3] cultivated *Sedum Clusianum*, and the leaves at once began to assume a flatter character, and he remarks as a coincidence that the two species *S. stellatum* and *S. tuberosum*, which are not rupicolous in France, but inhabit wet places, have flat leaves. On the other hand, I have found those of *S. stellatum* growing in cracks between flat slabs of rock in

---

[1] The succulency of several members of the *Chenopodiaceæ* which frequent saline marshes and deserts may be now attributed to the same cause.

[2] With regard to the leaves of *Haworthia* and *Gasteria*, M. Lanza observes (*Malpighia*, iv. p. 145–167, 1890), that the surface is covered with excrescences originating from below the epidermis and composed of colourless cells, the function of which appears to be to protect the plant from excessive insolation. The leaves of *Haworthia fasciata* altogether change their habit with the locality in which they grow, being flat or erect according as they are exposed to shade or to sunlight. (Quoted from the *Journ. Roy. Mic. Soc.*, 1891, p. 66.

[3] *Bull. de la Soc. Bot. de Fr.*, 1886, p. 191.

D

Malta, in an exposed, heated spot, were more or less cylindrical.
M. Battandier also says that two other species which are not
rupicolous but grow in dry earth, viz., *S. rubens* and *S. Mag-
noli*, have flat leaves in a wet season, but cylindrical leaves in
a dry one.

Similarly, the common maritime fleshy samphire of temperate climates, *Crithmum maritimum*, when cultivated in a
garden became luxuriant and bore flat and smooth leaves.

Centaurea crassifolia, a plant peculiar to the Maltese islands,
growing in hot rocky valleys, has thick succulent leaves which
survive during the hot season, but in March, when it begins to
produce its new foliage, before the hot summer has approached,
I found that the leaves were nearly as thin as of ordinary
plants.

As another example, M. Constantin observed [1] that *Salsola
Kali*, a common inhabitant of maritime salt marshes, grows up
sandy rivers, when it passes into *S. Tragus* by losing the usual
character of its leaves.

The most elaborate series of experiments to test the source
of the succulency of maritime plants has been carried out by
M. Lesage, [2] who shows conclusively that the presence of salt
is at least a potent cause in its production. He succeeded in
making plants, such as garden-cress, succulent by watering
them with salt water. He also testifies to the hereditary
effects, in that seed obtained from plants of cress which were
somewhat succulent in the first year's experiment, became still
more so in the following.

The increased substance of the leaf is accompanied by a
greater development of palisade tissue with diminished intercellular passages and a less proportion of chlorophyll. This

---

[1] *Journ. de Bot.*, 15 Mars 1887.
[2] *Rev. Gén. de Bot.*, vol. ii. pp. 55, 100, 163. See also *Comptes Rendus*,
cxii. 1891, p. 672.

latter result is correlated with a decrease in the amount of starch produced.

From all the above facts, natural and experimental, the conclusion is inevitable that while succulency is of benefit to the plants under the conditions in which they grow, especially by enabling them to store water during the hot and dry season, it is in all cases actually brought about by the direct action of the environment itself, coupled with the responsiveness of the protoplasm of the plant.

PROTECTION OF BUDS.—A feature very characteristic of the African desert grasses may be here mentioned, namely, the retention of the leaf-sheaths, so that the annual buds are carefully protected against drought when they appear in the spring. Similarly the *Paronychiaceæ* are provided with scarious stipules, completely concealing the buds within them ; similarly *Lavandula atriplicifolia* has a spike of densely overlapping bracts (resembling the "wheat-eared" monstrous form of *Dianthus*) protecting the flower-buds. Professor Warming noticed the same thing in Brazil. He thus writes :—" Dans le groupe des Glumiflores (*Cypéracées* et *Graminées*) les feuilles sont étroites et raides ; presque toutes les espèces de ce groupe sont tuniquées au sens où M. Hackel a employé ce mot pour la première fois en 1889, c'est-à-dire que les bourgeons demeurent enveloppés et protégés par la base des feuilles qui persistent pendant longtemps, comme cela a lieu aussi dans le *Posidonia oceanica* (*Andropogon, Rhyncospora, Scirpus* sp., ·&c.)." [1]

In the African deserts numerous species of *Aristida* illustrate this fact. Lastly, it may be added that bulb-scales ·may become almost "woody" (*Allium Crameri*, &c.).

---

[1] For illustrations of such protections the reader is referred to Dr. Eug. Warming's paper on Lagôa Santa, where he figures *Rhynchospora Warmingii*, p. 191, and *Scirpus paradoxus*, p. 192.

Roots.—The organs hitherto considered are all above ground, but roots also exhibit features of self-adaptation to desert life in the enormous length they sometimes acquire. Dr. G. Volkens describes [1] how a young plant of *Monsonia nivea* of one year's growth may be seen between July and January to have a small rosette of three or four leaves while the roots may be twenty inches in length. Other plants may have roots two or more metres long. The Colocynth, he observes, has an enormous length of root in order to maintain its existence. It stands singly, has large herbaceous leaves, without any means of preventing an excess of transpiration, as a cut shoot fades within five minutes, and yet it flourishes unshadowed through the whole summer.

The great length of root in certain desert plants has been also noticed elsewhere. Thus Dr. Aitchison observed in Beluchistan that "several of the *Astragali* (*A. Kahiricus, Auganus, buchtormensis*) have long whip-like roots, the bark of which is employed as twine by the people. These roots are extracted in a very neat way, by attaching a loop of twine to the crown, passing a stick through the other end, and making it act as a lever." [2]

M. de Candolle has also called attention to the advantages of long roots in enabling the plants to resist extremes of temperature. He says :—" L'action de la température est très sensible à la surface des sols, et l'est moins à une certaine profondeur ; d'où il résulte : 1°. Que, dans un terrain donné, les plantes à racines profondes résistent mieux aux extrêmes de la température que celles à racines superficielles. 2°. Qu'une plante donnée résiste mieux aux extrêmes de la température dans un terrain plus compacte, ou moins bon conducteur du calorique, ou moins doué de la faculté rayonnante, que dans un sol ou

[1] *Op. cit.*, p. 7 (*supra*, p. 36).
[2] *Op. cit.*, p. 431 (*supra*, p. 37).

trop léger ou bon conducteur, ou rayonnant fortement le calorique. 3°. La nature des plantes et celle du sol étant données, les plantes résistent mieux au froid dans une atmosphère sèche, et à la chaleur dans une atmosphère humide." [1]

The cause of the long tap-roots of so many desert plants is the well-known responsive power of their apices to moisture, or hydrotropism. Similar phenomena may not infrequently be seen in England. Thus if, for example, the tip of the root of a seedling turnip gets into a field drain-pipe, it may grow to a length of some yards, of course never producing the turnip.[2] As water is often to be found at various depths below the surface of the desert, the roots, stimulated by ascending moisture, continue to grow downwards till they attain very great lengths.

DURATION.—Some desert plants are usually annuals, the majority being perennials.[3] A feature, however, which Dr. Volkens notices is that these characters are particularly liable to change in desert plants according to circumstances. Plants which nominally live but one year, as species of *Savignya*, *Polycarpon*, *Malva*, *Trigonella*, *Ifloga*, &c., may survive two or more years; while perennials like *Capparis*, *Tamarix*, *Nitraria*, *Retama*, *Acacia*, &c., often become annuals. The fact is, that it simply depends upon the depth to which the primary tap-root descends, so as to secure a more continuous supply of water below the surface, which enables the plant to survive the hot season.

Mr. Scott Elliot has observed the same fact in South Africa.[4]

---

[1] *Essai Élémentaire de Géographie Botanique; Dict. des Sci. Nat.*, tom. xviii.

[2] I have such a specimen, which was brought to the late Professor J. S. Henslow by a villager in Suffolk about the year 1850.

[3] Professor Warming found annuals to form only about 6 per cent. of the flora of the "Campos" (*Lagoa Santa*, p. 459).

[4] *Op. cit., Trans. Bot. Soc. Edin.*, 1891 (*supra*, p. 46).

In speaking of the prevalence of the "ericaceous" type, including 350 species of *Erica* itself, he remarks :—"It is not, I think, hard to see why this type should obtain so largely in the south-west district. There is, to begin with, no winter worthy of the name ; and therefore annuals would, when becoming acclimatised, probably cease dying at the end of the year, because there is no reason why they should. Certain European annuals of cultivation have, in fact, become perennials."

Now the annual, biennial, or perennial character of plants is often regarded as specific ; but it is one which can be easily changed, and may then become hereditary ; thus the garden form of the carrot is *now* biennial, but normally, as a wild plant, *Daucus Carota*, it is an annual. This is simply the result of sowing the seed of the original wild form *late in the season.* The consequence was that the plants did not blossom till the following year. Then, by selection, this biennial feature has been fixed, and is now hereditary. *Poa annua*, if grown in plenty of moisture, at once becomes a perennial, as it does also on the Alps, just as several other annuals at lower altitudes as well as latitudes become perennial when growing at higher altitudes and latitudes.

Mr. Th. Holm[1] has recorded a number of examples of American plants which are ordinarily annuals, but become perennial under exceptional conditions. They include *Hypericum nudicaule, Delphinium Consolida, Cyperus flavescens, Carex cyperoides*, and species of grasses and Crucifers which are annuals in Europe but perennials in the United States, and particularly so near Washington. For example, *Arabis dentata*, which is typically biennial, and *A. lyrata*, which is normally annual or biennial, have formed perennial specimens. On the

[1] On the Vitality of some Annual Plants ; *Amer. Journ. Sci.*, xlii. 1891, p. 304 ; see also *Rev. Gén. de Bot.*, 1892, p. 364.

contrary, *A. lævigata*, said to be perennial by Hildebrandt, is not at all rare as a biennial near Washington.

This change in duration may be accompanied by a change in the period of flowering, or the period of flowering may change without a plant altering its duration of life, and these alterations may become permanent. Thus Sir J. D. Hooker [1] noticed how the Stock and Mignonette become perennials in Tasmania; on the other hand, the Castor-oil becomes an annual in England.

As a remarkable instance of a plant having undergone a complete change of season in flowering, *Oxalis cernua* may be mentioned. This is a native of the Cape of Good Hope and flowers in the winter, *i.e.*, July; but throughout the whole of the Mediterranean border, where *it has* become dispersed since 1806, it blossoms from November to April.[2]

Darwin has so fully discussed, under the head of "Acclimatisation,"[3] the variability of plants in adapting themselves to climate and so becoming "precocious" or "late" in flowering, that I need not enter upon this subject. All I would contend for is, that such variations of habit are simply due to the responsiveness of protoplasm to the environmental conditions, and that, when once acquired, they all tend to and may become hereditary traits.

In corroboration of this I will conclude with the following observations by the late Dr. Lindley :[4]—

"It often happens that, as in peas, the tendency in such plants to advance or retard their season of ripening *was originally connected with the soil or climate* in which they grew. A plant which for years is cultivated in a warm dry soil, where it ripens

---

[1] Animals and Plants under Domestication, ii. p. 305.

[2] See my paper on "The Northern Distribution of Oxalis cernua, Thunb. ;" *Proc. Linn. Soc.*, 1890–92, p. 31.

[3] Animals and Plants under Domestication, ii. 306.

[4] Theory of Horticulture, p. 465 (the italics are mine).

in forty days, *will acquire habits of great excitability ;* and when sown in another soil, will, for a season or so, retain its habit of rapid maturity ; and the reverse will happen to an annual from a cold and wet soil. But, as the latter will gradually become excitable and precocious if sown for a succession of seasons in a dry warm soil, so will the former lose those habits and become late and less excitable."

CHAPTER III

HISTOLOGICAL PECULIARITIES OF DESERT PLANTS

ALTHOUGH the morphological features of desert plants are obviously adaptive, the histological elements illustrate the same fact even in the most minute details.[1]

EPIDERMIS AND CUTICLE.—Commencing with the epidermis, a thickened cuticle in various degrees is of well-nigh universal occurrence. There is also very frequently a superficial layer of wax. The cuticle is often covered with waved lines or ridges, especially on elevated cells, and the hairs with tubercles.

M. Dufour[2] found experimentally that the thickness of the external and lateral walls of epidermal cells is greater under sunlight than is that of the same species when grown in the shade, and the cuticle is also much more developed under sunlight.

It need hardly be pointed out that in the desert the sunlight and glare reflected from the sand is very powerful, and therefore, cæteris paribus, the intensification of those elements mentioned is·just what would be on à priori grounds expected from M. Dufour's experiments. But the thickness of the cuticle tends·powerfully to prevent the loss of water, which

---

[1] The reader might consult M. Vesque's descriptions and figures of species of *Capparis*, showing how their anatomical structure conformed to their habits. " *L'Espèce Végétale considérée au Point de Vue de l'Anatomie comparée;* " *Ann. Sci. Nat.*, Sér. 6, tom. xiii. 1882, p. 5.

[2] *Ann. des Sci. Nat. Bot.*, Sér. 7, tom. v. p. 311, tom. viii.

is the end and aim of all desert plants in their adaptations to the climate.

Dr. Volkens[1] observed that a considerable number of xerophile plants are protected against a too energetic transpiration by the existence on the surface, outside the cuticle, of a thick layer of a sort of varnish, very brilliant in appearance. It is in most part soluble in alcohol, and without doubt of a resinous nature. An interesting fact, from the point of view of geographical botany, is that such plants are peculiar to the Southern hemisphere.

The presence of wax on the surface of leaves was long ago observed (by Mulder) to be closely correlated with chlorophyll, so that when we find the palisadic layers much increased, as they are in desert plants, we should à priori expect a specially increased layer of wax. The production of this substance is dependent ultimately upon the increased amount of light [and heat?], which appears to deoxidise chlorophyll and to leave wax as one of the products; hence the epidermis becomes colourless and the cuticle coated with wax, as the wax increases with the loss of water. Upon this Mr. Herbert Spencer observes: "The deposit of waxy substance next to the outer surface of the cuticular layer in leaves is probably initiated by the evaporation [transpiration?] which it eventually checks."[2]

When the external walls of epidermal cells are flat, the cuticle is generally smooth; when, on the contrary, each cell forms a convexity towards the exterior, it is nearly always ornamented either with parallel and straight or undulating striæ, or they may be more or less reticulated, &c. The above features are common on desert plants. M. Vesque offers the

---

[1] *Ueber Pflanzen mit lackirten Blättern. Berichte der deutschen botan. Gesellschaft*, Bd. viii. Heft 4, p. 120, 1890.

[2] Principles of Biology, ii. p. 245.

following interpretation:[1]—"Il serait bien difficile de déterminer le rôle de ces dessins cuticulaires par l'expérience ; mais étant donnée cette circonstance singulière que les épidermes plans en sont ordinairement dépourvus, tandis que les parties convexes en présentent presque toujours, il est permis d'émettre une hypothèse à mes yeux fort plausible. Chaque cellule convexe représente en effet une lentille convergente qui, malgré ses faibles dimensions, peut, surtout dans les pays chauds, notablement surélever la température en un point déterminé de la cellule épidermique ; il est donc important, dans ce cas, de remplacer la vitre lisse par une vitre cannelée qui a pour effet de disperser, d'égaliser la lumière incidente ; de cette manière on comprend pourquoi, dans un grand nombre de cas, les cellules convexes qui avoisinent les stomates ou les poils enfoncés au-dessous du niveau de l'épiderme, et celles qui se relèvent en petites saillies autour de la base des poils, sont striées tandis que les autres ne le sont pas."

As far as sheets of glass with striated and reticulated surfaces can imitate a cuticle, I find that a sheet of sensitive paper is not darkened to the same extent under the former as under a clear sheet of glass of the same thickness, when fully exposed, and for the same time, to sunlight, though nothing could be deduced from any differences of temperature under the same circumstances.

PILOSISM.—Since a more or less excessive hairiness is a characteristic feature of the great majority of plants growing in hot and barren deserts, the question arises as to what is the cause.   Now, any extra outgrowth, even if it be but epidermal trichomes, implies the presence of more nutritive materials at the disposal of the plant at the spot than when they are not formed at all.   M. Mer, who studied the question, came to

---

[1] *Op. cit.*, p. 34 (*supra*, p. 44, note).

the conclusion that, *cæteris paribus*, hairs are due to a localised extra nourishment, and therefore frequently occur upon the ribs and veins, *i.e.*, immediately over the channels of sap. He thinks this view is supported by such a case, *e.g.*, as *Rhus Cotinus*, in which the abortive pedicels, which bear no fruit, develop a large amount of hairs, while the pedicels which bear fruit have few or none. The excess of hair is therefore presumably due to a compensatory distribution of sap.

M. Aug. Pyr. de Candolle came to the same conclusion in 1827; for he then wrote about *Rhus Cotinus* as follows:— "Peut-être la sève destinée à nourir les fruits, ne trouvant plus d'emploi lorsque ceux-ci ont avorté, produit-elle ce développement extraordinaire de poils. Quelques filets d'étamines (*Verbascum, Tradescantia*) deviennent aussi poilus quand les anthères avortent, et probablement par la même cause." [1]

Dr. M. T. Masters observes, when speaking of the hair on the barren pedicels of *Rhus Cotinus*, or the "Wig-plant," as it is called:—"A similar production of hair may be noticed in many cases where the development of a branch or of a flower is arrested; and this occurs with especial frequency where the arrest in growth is due to the puncture of an insect or to the formation of a gall." [2]

As another illustration of this last-mentioned fact, it may often be noticed how *Veronica Chamædrys* terminates its shoots with an excessively woolly globular bud. A similar thing happens to a heath, *Erica scoparia*, common on the hills around Cannes. In the latter plant the abnormal leaves are broad, ovate, and densely hairy, while the ordinary leaves are linear and glabrous. These globular structures in both plants are due to the irritation set up by the presence of grubs. The axis and the innermost leaves are arrested at the apex, while

---

[1] *Organographie Végétale*, tom. i. pp. 111, 112.
[2] *Teratology*, p. 472.

in compensation the lower leaves of the bud alter their character, enlarge and become densely clothed with hair.[1]

The fact of hairs being developed over and about the fibro-vascular cords is of common occurrence, and under the above aspect becomes very significant in such cases as in desert grasses, Lavender, &c. Pfitzer observes :—" Almost all grasses inhabiting very dry localities have leaves with well-marked longitudinal folds ; "[2] the stomata being situated within the grooves, while the ridges correspond to the vascular and fibrous cords. The tooth-like hair of the grasses (or branched, as, e.g., on the calyx of Lavender) project like *chevaux-de-frise* over the grooves. They have swollen bases capable of imbibing moisture ; and so in all probability absorb dew, as well as protect the surface against a loss of water. The marginal inrolling of the blade is of course an additional protection. To such an extent does this occur, that many blades of desert grasses are perfectly cylindrical ; the upper surface, which is the especially grooved one, being entirely concealed from view, as may be well seen in Volkens' figure of *Aristida ciliata*.[3] In some cases, as in this grass, certain hairs assume a papillate form immediately over the stomata.

Besides the presence of grooves on leaves, there are several genera and species which are practically leafless, the young shoots performing the functions usually attributable to leaves. Such plants are characteristic of dry localities. Their stems have strongly marked similar characteristics. The chief of these are, allowing for variations, more or less deep longitudinal grooves in the surface, at the bottom of which are the stomata,

---

[1] I have elsewhere called attention to this fact in its analogy with the results of the irritating action of the pollen-tube. See "Origin of Floral Structures," p. 164 *seq.*

[2] Quoted by De Bary, *Comp. Anat., &c.*, p. 50.

[3] *Op. cit.*, pl. xvii. fig. 4 (*supra*, p. 36).

with or without protecting hairs. Strong masses of scleren-chymatous tissues are present, often pervading the stem in a radial direction, with a large-celled thick-walled pith and en-larged medullary rays. These latter act as an aqueous storage tissue. As examples which I have had the opportunity of exa-mining are species of Tamarisk trees and of Casuarina, often cultivated in Cairo; of desert plants, *Retama retem*, *Pity ranthus tortuosus*, *Statice pruinosa*, &c. In Europe we have the Furze and Broom as representing similar features, while in Australia, besides *Casuarina*, there are species of *Cytisus*, the names illustrating the same feature, as *C. Ephedrioides*, *C. Equisetifolia*, &c.[1]

As another illustration which serves to support M. Mer's contention that hairs are, *cæteris paribus*, a result of compensa-tion, M. Lesage[2] found in a root of the second order of *Phaseolus*, which was much longer than the primary root, that the portion *outside* the water was covered with numerous root-hairs; *near* the water these hairs were elongated, while *in* the water they were much shorter, and finally disappeared alto-gether. In a transverse section it was 'seen that the cortical layers in the air contained smaller elements than those in the water, and in the central cylinder the xylem was proportion-ately more lignified in the aërial portion.

The root of the bean was made the subject of similar ob-servations. It was found that when numerous secondary roots were suppressed, the primary root was covered with numerous absorbing hairs.

The above interpretation will therefore satisfactorily explain the existence of the hairiness of plants in deserts; for drought,

---

[1] For illustrations the reader is referred to Volkens, *op. cit.* ; Boodle and Worsdell on "Casuarina, "Annals of Botany," viii. pl. xv.; " "Natural History of Plants," by Kerner and Oliver, 4. p. 299.

[2] *Comptes Rendus*, cxii. 1891, p. 109.

aided by the barrenness of the soil, tends to arrest the development of parenchymatous tissues; and in proportion as this arrest is excessive, so is the compensating process of the production of hairs. Hence, just as with plenty of water, or a good soil, as obtains under cultivation, plants tend to become less hairy than in the wild state, as, *e.g.*, the parsnip; so, conversely, under aridity and a poor soil hairiness becomes a characteristic and hereditary feature.

Here again, therefore, if the above explanation of M. Mer be true, the very conditions which bring about the production of an excessive clothing of hair, are precisely those against the severity of which the dense clothing is one of the very best of protections.

The above interpretation receives indirectly an additional countenance from the fact that just those desert plants which *do* develop much parenchyma and become excessively fleshy, as the *Aloineæ, Euphorbia, Cactaceæ, Zygophyllum,* &c., are generally entirely hairless.

Intense hairiness is certainly one of the most conspicuous features of desert plants, and is an invaluable means of lessening the heat by forming a non-conducting surface, and, on the other hand, as a means of absorbing dew during the summer when no rain falls.

Dr. G. Volkens remarks that a multitude of cases establish the empirical deduction that drought is correlated with the presence of much hair, though what the real causal connection may be is not clear to him.[1] He observed that as transpiration tends to increase, so does the relative quantity of hair, till (it may be added) the quantity becomes so great as to check the very process which may have had something to do with bringing it about.

---

[1] He makes no allusion to M. Mer's observations, which were probably, therefore, unknown to him.

In desert plants the hairs are of different forms. They may be stiff, straight, and adpressed to the surface, all lying in one direction; or the "needles" are interlacing, or the hairs may be of a twisted cottony character and cover the surface with a layer of wool; or, again, they may be stellate and flat, the branches interlacing so as to produce a dense coating of felt; or they may be bladdery and filled with water. These latter may finally collapse, dry up, and form a glassy sheet over the surface of the leaf.

There are also peculiarities in the structure of the hairs themselves which are remarkable. In many cases the cavity is quite filled up with the exception of the broad basal part of the cell, while the outer surface may be densely coated with wax, either entirely or with "gashes" and "pores" (*Diplotaxis Harra*), or else the basal portion is quite devoid of it (*Heliotropium luteum*), so that water can readily pass from without into the interior. Dr. Volkens observes with regard to the filling up of the lumen with cellulose matter, that this is connected with the swelling up of the inner membrane, and shows (by treatment with suitable re-agents) that it is a substance which, when water is absorbed, can hold it fast with great strength. This of course greatly retards transpiration.

I have found in some cases, besides the closely applied felt, that there are taller branching hairs, standing much above the level (*Erucaria Aleppica*). These I take to be specially absorbing hairs, as well as all which have no wax, or at least places on the hairs where it is wanting.

As a special peculiarity, I have found in *Cocculus* (*Menispermum*) *Leæba* a basket-like arrangement of hairs round the auxiliary buds. This would presumably retain a large drop of dew, by means of which the bud would be benefited.

Besides being actual absorbents of dew,[1] it may be borne in mind that not only does the felt collect the dewdrops which get entangled in it, and so get absorbed, but it parts with them by evaporation much more slowly than does a smooth leaf, as I have tested by experiments with many kinds of leaves.

Now, Dr. Volkens observes, though he *suspected* it, he cannot say for certain how or why the hairiness is produced. But besides the reasonable interpretation of M. Mer which I have given above, that hairiness is a direct result of the environmental action upon the plant is established by numerous cases. In the first place, we have "the argument of coincidences," as I would call it; but when we find that a change of habitat brings about a greater or less degree of hairiness, the *probabilities* accumulate till they amount to a moral conviction, which is further established by experimental verification. Thus, for example, the hairiness of wild plants tends to decrease under cultivation, as in the wild parsnip. Linnæus observed this fact nearly two hundred years ago, for he says :[2]—"Spinas et hirsutiem plantæ sæpius exuunt a loco vel cultura." *Ranunculus repens* growing in a dry barren gravelly soil is very hairy, but a plant growing in water ten feet from one of the former kind, which I have preserved, is scarcely hairy at all.

M. Battandier observes[3] that *Bellis Atlantica*, with leaves covered with a true velvet having a long pile, at the summit of the mountain Blida, when cultivated in Algeria bore leaves less and less velvety, till they finally became as glabrous as the

---

[1] That plants can absorb rain and dew by their green parts, I would refer the reader to my paper "On the Absorption of Rain and Dew by the Green Parts of Plants," *Journ. Linn. Soc. Bot.*, xvii. p. 313.

[2] *Philos. Bot.*, 272.

[3] *Bull. de la Soc. Bot. de Fr.*, 1887, p. 193.

Bellis of Algeria. Similarly *Allium Chamœmoly*, when cultivated for eight years, lost its villosity which it had on the
summit of Zaccar. So also *Cerastium Boissieri*, which is
white and tomentose at the summit of Ait-Ouabau, became
glabrous and of a beautiful green at Algiers.

Hairiness is well known to be a most variable character,
and although it is recognised as specific when constant and
abundant, as in *Verbascum*, and therefore less variable, it
obviously becomes much less important when it fluctuates.

It may be observed here that the hairiness as a hereditary character varies greatly. Thus M. Battandier found that
Bellis Atlantica varied *when transplanted*, yet when raised by
seed in Algeria it did not show similar modifications; similarly
Allium Chamœmoly, though it became less villous, remained
more hairy than its congeners after cultivation as well as by
sowing. On the other hand, seedlings of *Pastinaca sativa*,
raised in a prepared border in the Botanic Gardens of the
Cirencester Agricultural College, became less and less hairy,
and finally quite glabrous.[1] As a spontaneous variety, *Malva
parviflora* may be mentioned; as grown in the Nile valley as
a culinary vegetable it is not very hairy, the hairs being
stellate, having only a few rays, sometimes two only. As a
desert plant, where it appears as a small annual for a few
weeks only, the stellate hairs increase their number of rays.
Similarly *Erodium laciniatum* is much less hairy when growing in waste ground on Rhoda Island in the Nile by Cairo
than when in the desert. I find that the main differences
between the two forms may be summed up as follows :—
Hypodermic collenchyma is much thicker in the petiole of

---

[1] Professor Buckman raised the "domesticated" variety alluded to, in
1847, which he called the "Student." It is still regarded as the "best
variety" in cultivation, according to Messrs. Sutton & Sons of Reading
(1895).

the desert form. The upper epidermis has its cells similar in size, but with more hairs. The lower epidermis has cells which are much smaller than those of the Nile-valley form. The palisade consisting of two rows of cells is identical in both cases below the upper epidermis; but while there is a lax mesophyll of rounded cells on the lower side in the Nile-valley form, the corresponding cells are somewhat elongated in shape, thus tending to assume the palisadic type characteristic of the lower side as well as of the upper in the desert form. Hairs of the latter are more numerous in proportion of twenty-four to ten for the same area.

STOMATA.—These structures are frequently sunk below the level of the outer surface of the leaf, and may occur on both sides. The depression in which they lie is either in consequence of the great thickness of the outer wall of the epidermis (*Allium Crameri, Pityranthus tortuosus*, &c.), or because the epidermis itself lines cavities in the parenchyma, which are either naked or clothed with hairs covering over the stomata, as in the grass *Danthonia Forskali*, very like the well-known case of *Nerium Oleander*, to which M. Vesque adds *Capparis Breynia*.[1] The Oleander has narrow, rigid, more or less erect leaves, which are well suited to live in a dry atmosphere. In a specimen growing at Cannes, there was a thick cuticle and two layers of thick-walled hypodermic cells, a palisade tissue of two layers on the upper side, and of one layer on the lower. A lax mesophyll of green cells fills up the central space. The stomata are on the bottom of the epidermal cavities.

In a leaf gathered from a tree in Cairo there were slight differences, in that there happened to be no palisade cells on the lower side at all, the lax mesophyll reaching to the hypodermic layer. Such differences are probably accidental, but

[1] *L'Espèce Vég.*, &c.; *Ann. des Sci. Nat. Bot.*, 1882, 6 Sér. tom. xiii.

they show clearly how easily the anatomy of a leaf conforms to slight differences of illumination, &c.

In desert plants the guard cells are often so thick-walled that the lumen is nearly obliterated; and contrary to what is generally supposed to be the case in temperate regions, Dr. Volkens shows that they often close during the day and are open at night.[1] Perhaps the arrested moisture, due to the check to transpiration, may cause turgescence by day, which closes the slit, while its cessation at night brings about a relaxation; or it may be the result of a more complicated action between the guard-cells and the adjacent epidermal cells. It is, however, difficult to say without a very close investigation into the phenomena on the living plants in their natural conditions.

ASSIMILATIVE TISSUES.—The chlorophyll tissue of an ordinary dorsi-ventral leaf is typically differentiated into a palisadic layer below the upper epidermis and a spongy layer above the lower epidermis. It is well known that in those plants in which the leaf is normally reversed in position, as *Alstrœmeria*, the relative positions of these two layers are also reversed. This inversion can be more or less decidedly brought about by compelling certain leaves to develop their surfaces reversed. Moreover, when leaves assume a vertical position, so as to be equally illuminated on both sides, then the epidermis and subjacent palisadic tissues are also more or less alike; as in some grasses, the phyllodes of Australian Acacias, the pendulous falcate leaves of gum-trees, though the first-formed horizontal leaves on the same gum-trees are dorsi-ventral in structure, like ordinary horizontal leaves.[2]

---

[1] *Die Flora der Ægypt.-Arab. Wüste*, p. 47.

[2] The chief differences between the two forms of leaves in *Eucalyptus* I find to be as follows :—In the horizontal leaf the upper epidermis is composed of small cells, and there are no stomata. There is a palisade

M. G. Briosi has written a voluminous work with many plates upon the leaves of *Eucalyptus globulus*, Labil, to which the reader is referred for numerous details.[1]

The preceding facts all conspire to prove that the differentiation of the mesophyll into palisadic tissue is the direct result of illumination ; and that as the upper surface of normally horizontal leaves receives more light than the lower, the differentiation of the chlorophyll cells into an elongated form parallel to the incident light is the direct outcome, *cæteris paribus*, of that external agent.

A significant fact with regard to these alterations is that the change evinces itself by degrees. Thus in young leaves of *Alstrœmeria psittacina*, M. Dufour [2] shows that it is only partially effected. Thus the first leaf stands vertically. It possesses few stomata, and is nearly alike on both sides. The second leaf is still nearly vertical, being only twisted towards the apex. It has stomata on both faces at the base, but at the point shows many upon the upper, but none on the lower side: The subsequent leaves have the petiole twisted, and are completely reversed in position. Their petioles have a small number of stomata on the two faces ; the limb, exclusively upon the superior face, now becomes the lower in position.

tissue of one layer of cells, with lax mesophyll below the lower epidermis. This latter has larger cells than the upper and is provided with stomata. The pendulous leaf is a good deal thicker than the horizontal. Both epidermides are provided with a very dense cuticle in which the stomata are deep-seated. There are four rows of palisade cells on both sides with a chlorophyllous mesophyll between them. The petiole is flattened, so that the leaf can swing much in the same way as that of the Poplar. The horizontal leaves in *E. globulus* are sessile.

[1] *Intorno alla Anatomia delle Foglie dell' Eucalyptus globulus, Labil,* 95 pp. et 23 pl., Milano, 1891.

[2] *Bull. de la Soc. de Bot. de Fr.*, 28 Mai 1886, p. 269. The author here gives several references to the literature of the subject.

Another interesting point is that in young leaves the meso-phyll is homogeneous ; but the cells under the upper epidermis are rather larger at first in the older leaves, showing an here-ditary tendency to develop palisadic tissue ; but later on the influence of the light soon renders the cells below the—now reversed—inferior side much longer than the others.

The needle-like leaves of the Norway Spruce prove, accord-ing to the careful investigations of M. Mer,[1] to be most re-markably sensitive to light, becoming more quadrilateral, with a uniform palisadic tissue, as the leaf grows more exposed, but flatter and more dorsi-ventral when it is more shaded on the same tree.

He also observes the remarkable result of frost setting up a "habit" in the tree as follows :—"Trees planted isolated have some modifications. They become more bushy, from the development of lateral buds, which are arrested in forests. When the young shoots are struck by frosts in the spring, it happens at times that, without reaching the point of death, they lose their turgescence. They become soft, · and their extremity turns toward the ground. Lignification supervenes before they have recovered their turgescence, and they remain thus definitely curved. When the terminal bud is not de-stroyed it develops its succeeding shoot the following year in this position.

"If one places it vertically, the terminal bud turns down-wards, and the branch in course of development preserves this situation ; or rather its extremity tends to elevate itself by a slight curvature. This depends upon its degree of vigour and the time during growth when the experiment is made."

This passage is very suggestive as a cause of "weeping" varieties of trees, by a *temporary* injury producing a *per-*

---

[1] *Bull. de la Soc. de Bot. de Fr.*, 1883, p. 40.

manent effect in the growth, though not to the extent of being hereditary.

Again, Dr. F. Noll[1] has shown that external influences determine not only the *direction* of some organs, but also the *position* in which they are formed; as, *e.g.*, the development of the gemmæ of *Marchantia*, of aërial roots on climbing plants, &c. In other and more numerous cases the formation of fresh organs appears to be independent of external forces, and to be determined only by the internal, *i.e.*, hereditary forces, in the plants; as, for instance, in the dorsi-ventral structure of many parts of plants. In *Bryopsis* the reversal of the plant brings about a corresponding internal organic transformation.

Professor Eug. Warming notes the same feature in the leaves of plants growing in the arid campos of Lagoa Santa. He says:[2]—"La direction des feuilles accuse également la sécheresse du climat; beaucoup d'entre elles ont habituellement une direction verticale ou sont au moins très relevées, de manière à n'être frappées par les rayons solaires que sous un angle aigu. Certaines espèces ont des feuilles très réduites, et quelques-unes sont aphylles; elles appartiennent à des familles très différentes." The reader will perceive that this description would apply equally well to many desert plants of the Northern Hemisphere.

Applying the preceding observation to desert plants;—if a leaf be small, narrow, and moreover assume a more or less vertical position, as is so generally the case, so that it is illuminated nearly equally on both sides, we should expect to find on *à priori* grounds that it would have a palisade tissue on both sides. Such is precisely the case with innumerable desert plants. The only, and indeed relatively rare exceptions

---

[1] See *Journ. Roy. Micr. Soc.*, 1891, p. 490.

[2] *Op. cit.*, p. 157 (*supra*, p. 3).

are in the leaves of such plants as develop their foliage during the rainy season as annuals, or in. "Nile-valley" plants which happen to secure a place on the borders of the desert. Such have a more or less characteristic spongy parenchyma on the under side, while transitions from this to true palisadic tissue are easy to be found.

The typical chlorophyll tissue in leaves of true desert plants is therefore palisadic on both sides, the cells being arranged in from one to four, or even five superposed rows. These sometimes meet in the middle (*Zizyphus Spina-Christi*); in others there is a central layer of short rounded cells (*Cassia obovata*), the usual lax merenchyma being entirely wanting.

In addition to the typical palisadic cells at right angles to the surface, large cells, palisadic in shape, may be arranged in cylinders around the fibro-vascular bundles. This is particularly well seen in grasses, but within this cylinder is a second, of chlorophyllous cells, which are quadrate and short in form. This peculiar arrangement of a double cylinder of green cells is not confined to grasses, but occurs in exogens, as *Tribulus alatus, Atriplex Halimus*, &c., so that in all cases the fibro-vascular cords are densely embedded in chlorophyllous tissue.

In some cases the inner sheath is colourless and acts as a water-storage tissue (*Oligomeris subulata*). It is, I think, really homologous with the endoderm.

M. Dufour [1] found that chlorophyllous tissue is much more developed in sunlight than in shade; and it may be added that a similar phenomenon occurs in Alpine plants and plants of high latitudes as compared with the same species growing at low altitudes and latitudes.[2] In these cases the deeper green tint is also due to the uninterrupted sunlight. Hence

---

[1] *Ann. des Sci. Nat. Bot.*, Sér. 7, tom. v. p. 311.
[2] *Ibid.*, 1879.

it is not surprising to find the chlorophyll tissues reach a high development under the intense light in the desert, whether from the sun direct or reflected upwards from the sand.

LIGNEOUS TISSUES.—Messrs. Dr. D. H. Scott and G. Brebner have described[1] the histology of *Acantholimum glumaceum* (*Plumbaginea*), and Professor D. Oliver had previously examined[2] that of *Acanthophyllum* as well (*Caryophyllea*). These are both desert plants, and I might now add a great many more anomalous and sub-anomalous stems of plants growing in the North African deserts, some of which Dr. G. Volkens has described and figured.[3] The general conclusion deducible from a study of their peculiarities is, that these are all due to the climatic conditions under which they grow. Summing them up, they may be enumerated as follows:—There is a general tendency to lignification, with an absence of medullary rays, (*Zilla myagroides, Bassia muricata*) ; if they be present, they are comparatively few and have thick walls (*Farsetia africana, Helianthemum kahiricum, Ochradenus baccatus*). The fibro-vascular cords may form "islands," as seen in a transverse section, embedded in dense tissues (*Statice pruinosa, Atriplex leucocladum, Pityranthus tortuosus*) ; the "wedges" of wood may fail to form a regular zone, but be more or less isolated and . embedded in water-storage tissue (*Tamarix mannifera, Anabasis articulata*). The wood may be deeply indented with cortical invasions, as Professor Oliver has shown to be the case in *Acanthophyllum*. Dr. Scott observes that this is due to the fact that the zone does not close up after having early parted with a cord for an appendicular organ. I think we may attribute this failure to a want of activity in the

[1] *Ann. of Bot.*, vol. v. p. 259.
[2] *Trans. Linn. Soc.*, vol. xxii. p. 289.
[3] *Die Flora der Ægyptisch-Arabischen Wüste, &c.*

formation of wood, which may be correlated to the insufficiency of foliage during the hot months.[1] Perhaps the
curious cavities described [2] by Professor D. Oliver in a species
of *Acantholimum* as occurring in the wood may be attributed
to the same cause.

As other examples of anomalous stems, Dr. Volkens describes and figures that of *Gypsophila Rokejeka ;* the pericycle
(which is often very active in the Caryophylleæ) puts on a
very dense zone of thick-walled sclerenchyma in lieu of
xylem, which in this plant is comparatively feeble. A similar
result occurs in *Telephium sphærospermum*, of the allied order
Paronychiaceæ. I have found an analogous result of pericycular activity in *Iphiona mucronata*. Inside a cortex there
are zones of square, oblong, or irregular-shaped patches of
sclerogen embedded in a parenchymatous tissue,[3] and only
isolated patches of xylem around the medulla, all being
embedded in a "stereome-zone." *Astragalus Forskali* has a
very anomalous stem. It has large cords of liber outside a
zone of cork, then another series outside the phloëm, a third
complete zone in the middle of that tissue. An anomalous
xylem follows, surrounding a medulla, in the centre of which
is a column of collenchyma! To this I would add the stem
of *Anabasis articulata*, which has only rudiments of leaves,
opposite and distichous. All the elements, as seen in a
transverse section, make up four series of crescent-shaped
structures around an hour-glass shaped pith. Taking a
"wedge," there is sclerenchyma forming the angle, then a

---

[1] I find that Grisebach confirms this idea, for in speaking of the partially developed wood in *Haloxylon Ammodendron*, he says :—"La suppres-
sion du feuillage détermine la croissance incomplète du corps ligneux."—
La Vég. du Globe, i. p. 630.

[2] *Loc. cit.*, tab. 51, fig. 24.

[3] Dr. Volkens figures a section of a *young* stem, but does not appear to
have noticed the development of pericycle.

zone of large vessels and wood fibres, then cortical parenchyma and sclerenchyma outside.

It may be observed that the four wedges roughly resembling a Maltese cross here appear to be correlated to the positions of the rudimentary leaves, the xylem tissues failing just where no leaves occur.

As long as the shoots are young and green, one may add to the above peculiarities of the stem the great thickness of the cuticular surface of the epidermis, which is not infrequently clothed with hair like that of the foliage ; the great depth of the palisadic layer, which often consists of three, four, or more zones of elongated cells (*e.g.*, *Zilla*), the cortex acting as a storage tissue for water, subsequently passing over into cork.

Now when we observe how often the different members of the tissues of the stems of woody desert plants are thus variously dispersed and constructed, while at the same time there are certain general features very commonly observed throughout, I think we cannot fail to arrive at the conclusion that these structures are simply the outcome of the environment in which such plants live. This view is corroborated by experiments, for they prove that the great tendency to lignification of the tissues, as already shown for the spinescent features, is a result of a deficiency of water, and they at once tend to disappear when desert plants grow in an ordinary prepared soil of cultivation. This, for example, is well seen in several species which frequent both the desert and the Nile valley, and in the plant of *Zilla myagroides* already alluded to, which was raised from seed in Cairo. The spines were quite flexible, the pericycular sclerenchyma, which is very dense and thick-walled in the desert plants, being very greatly reduced under cultivation.

We have also seen from Duchartre's experiment with *Dios-*

corea Batatas that the absence of water is a direct cause—in conjunction with the responsiveness of protoplasm—of a comparative increase of lignification. To this we may add the great defection of foliage in the hot summer months, when the formation of tissues is proportionately arrested. We can thus realise how anomalies in the structures of the stems may well be expected, though we may not be able to explain in the case of every individual stem the direct connection between cause and effect.

WATER-STORAGE TISSUES.—One of the most characteristic features of desert plants is their system of storing water. Commencing with the epidermis, certain of the cells form rounded or oval elongated bladders bulging on both sides; or they may elongate into hairs, the lower part acting as a storehouse of water; or they may assume the form of bladders supported on short pedicels. As an example is the familiar ice-plant which occurs about Alexandria, being so called because the water-cells are so conspicuous over the surface of the leaf. Many other plants are provided with them, but they are not so conspicuous to the naked eye. Thus species of *Reseda*, as *R. arabica, Gypsophila Rokejeka, Malcolmia ægyptiaca, Heliotropium arbaïnense, Hyoscyamus muticus,*[1] &c. *Atriplex leucocladum* has globular water-cells on slender supports. In this, as in *Atriplex Halimus*, the hairs finally collapse, and by sticking together form a sort of protecting sheath all over the surface of the leaf.

In the interior of the leaf the chlorophyll tissue is sometimes so abundant that the leaf is perfectly green throughout; in other cases the central tissue is nearly or quite devoid of

---

[1] The epidermal water-cells give a pale green colour to the leaf, and render it difficult to dry completely, except after many days in the press: perhaps because the water in all the plants is more or less thickened by gummy or other matters.

chlorophyll grains and acts as a storage tissue. In *Atriplex Halimus* the outer layer of the palisade cells is clear and. utilised as storage, while in some, as *Nitraria retusa*, large isolated storage cells lie embedded within the palisadic tissue; some others of the elongated cells being reservoirs of tannin.

Of the above varieties the central storage tissues is the most important, and is well seen, as it occupies by far the greater space, in such succulent leaves as those of *Mesembryanthemum* and *Aloë*. Sign. Arcangeli has lately observed that *Atriplex nummularia* possesses below the epidermis of the leaves an uncoloured parenchyma which covers the assimilative layer and represents a tissue of water-storage.[1]

In stems, the cortex and medulla act as storage tissues, the former gradually passing into cork, which of course is a great protective tissue in many desert plants.

Of subterranean structures, the bulb scales of species of *Allium*, *Pancratium*, &c., and the cortical region of roots of grasses may act as storage organs.

In some exogens the roots and subterranean stems assume special forms which act as reservoirs. Thus in the genus *Erodium* there are three desert species which develop tuberous . structures on the roots, which Dr. Volkens proved to be water- and not starch-storing tissues. This observation has been corroborated on quite independent grounds by Herr E. Hackel,[2] who has called attention to similar structures and their usage in certain grasses of dry climates; there being singular developments of the lowest internodes of the culms, shoots, and basal leaves.

---

[1] *Sulla Struttura delle Foglie del A. nummularia, Lindl., in Relazione alla Assimilazione* (*Nuovo Giorn. Bot. Ital.*, vol. xxii. p. 426).

[2] *Ueber einige Eigenthümlichkeiten der Gräser trockener Klimate. Verhandlungen der K.K. Zool. botan. Gesellsch.* Wien, Jahrgang 1890, p. 125.

He distinguished them as tuberous or bulbous grasses and
tunicated grasses. Tuberous grasses are such as *Phleum pra-
tense*, var. *nodosum*, Gaud., and *Arrhenatherum avenaceum*, var.
nodosum (*Avena nodosa*, L.), of which one or more of the basal
internodes of the culm and shoots attain a tuberous development; while *Poa bulbosa*, L , represents a bulbous grass, since
the bases of some of the sheaths of the leaves have increased
in thickness, and form a bulb very much like that of Allium.
He observed that these tuberous and bulbous forms *only* occur
in countries with periods of dry seasons, and none have been
observed in the moist parts of tropical regions.[1]

It is very interesting to learn that the author does not
consider these tubers and bulbs to be reservoirs of starch
or sugar, as are the similar organs of *Liliaceæ, Iridaceæ*, &c.,
though being structurally homologous with them ; but physiologically they are water reservoirs, just as Dr. Volkens maintains with regard to the tuberous roots of species of *Erodium*
in the deserts of North Africa.

What is particularly to be noticed is that Hackel has
shown that *Poa bulbosa*, on being cultivated in moist soil,
almost lost the bulbous character, clearly proving, there-

---

[1] Dr. Aitchison observed *Poa bulbosa* to be "the most common grass
covering the great plains of Beluchistan." (*Op. cit.*, p. 432, *supra*, p. 37).

Sir J. D. Hooker, speaking of desert plants, writes as follows :—" Though
invariable forms, they may be, and often are, themselves varieties or races
of a species that inhabits more fertile spots, as *Poa bulbosa*, which is a
very well-marked and constant form of *P. pratensis*, occurring in dry
sandy soil from England to North-Western India, its 'meadow' relative
being a very variable species in the same countries, and always struggling
for existence amongst other grasses, &c."—*Introduc. Essay to the Flora of
Tasmania*, 1859, p. xiii. note.

In his "Student's Flora of the British Isles," 3rd edit. 1884, this author
recognises *P. bulbosa* as a distinct species, "very near *P. alpina*, but
differing in locality, habit, and the close ovate panicle." *Poa bulbosa*
occurs on rocky ground in Malta, but not in the deserts of Egypt.

fore, that these productions are the direct result of a dry environment.

As another instance, of *Panicum bulbosum*, H. B. K. (regarded by Munro as a variety of *P. maximum*), of Southern United States, it is said :—"Its bulbous root-stocks contain a store of moisture which enables it to endure a protracted drought." [1]

These tuberous swellings on grasses are therefore clearly analogous with those on the roots of *Erodium*. Thus *E. hirtum* has globular, potato-like tubercles; *E. Hussoni*, finger-shaped ; and long, spindle-like roots occur in *E. glaucophyllum*. They all contain a storage tissue protected externally by a strong many-layered cortical coating. Their position being between the absorbing root-apices and the foliar transpiring surfaces, they act as reservoirs and regulate the supply of water.

Bulbs of species of *Allium*, as *A. Crameri*, &c., are similarly adapted to the desert, storing water within the inner scales, while the outermost series become almost woody in texture, as a protection against the hot sand in which they lie.

The cortex of roots acts as a storage tissue in many plants, as in *Gypsophila Rokejeka* and grasses, such as species of *Danthonia*, while the axis in both is densely woody.

A cause may be suggested for the development of the hypertrophic condition of the cortex and medulla of roots, which act as water-storage tissues, in the excessive heat which the sand surrounding the roots acquires from the sun. In the hottest months and hours of the day, the temperature, according to Dr. Volkens, sometimes rises to about 130° F. Now M. E. Prillieux [2] has shown experimentally how an abnormal excess of heat in the soil affects the roots of beans,

[1] Kew Bulletin, &c., Nov. 1894, p. 383.
[2] *Altérations produites dans les Plantes par la Culture dans un Sol surchauffé; Ann. des Sci. Nat.*, Sér. 6, tom. x. 1880, 347.

&c., in a precisely analogous manner, by enlarging the cells of the cortex and pith. While, however, in this latter case the distention of the parenchymatous tissue was, of course, abnormal and pathological, in the desert plants it has become a characteristic, important, and hereditary feature.

M. Battandier also calls attention to the fact that there are plants in which certain buds swell into tubercles capable of enduring the dry season, while the rest of the plant perishes; such are *Saxifraga globulifera* and *Sedum amplexicaule*. In Malta there are several species of *Ranunculus*, such as *R. bullatus*, which produce "root tubercles," which are thus enabled to survive the parching summer, and can live therefore in the most exposed surfaces round the fortifications of Valetta. *Romulea Bulbocodium* and *Iris Sisyrinchium* are similarly enabled to live and abound in barren rocky ground of Malta. This island has also fifteen species of *Allium*, nine of *Ophrys*, and eight of *Orchis*, as well as many other bulbous plants, which can thus survive the intense summer heat to which they are subjected; annuals being in a decided minority, except as weeds of cultivation.

From M. Hackel's observations on the tuberous processes in grasses which are formed in dry soil and disappear elsewhere, we at least have a strong suspicion, if nothing more, that all such structures are the outcome of the environment itself. This is also the conclusion of Mr. Scott Elliott, who notices how numerous are bulbous and tuberous plants in the Karoo of S. Africa. He says:—"Many orders have developed bulbs which usually show no trace of them, *e.g.*, the whole section *Hoarea* of *Pelargonium* is bulbous." This feature he attributes to the "direct influence of the climate." [1]

Finally, with regard to the origin of water-storage tissues

[1] Notes on the Regional Distribution of the Cape Flora ; *Trans. Bot. Soc. Edin.*, 1891, p. 241.

generally, I would suggest their being primarily due to the accumulation of water within the plant in consequence of the arrest of transpiration. This latter function is impeded in turn by the formation of a thick and often waxy cuticle and a dense clothing of hair, as well as by the secretion of substances (such as tannin, gum, mucilage, resinous matters, salts, &c.) which thicken the water and so render it less capable of vaporisation. But all these features, which thus bring about the very best structures to enable the plants to survive the injurious effects of the climate, are simply the direct outcome of the excessive heat and light coupled with the deficiency of water in the desert.

SECRETIONS. — These are of various kinds, and appear to play an important part in arresting a loss of water. Thus, tannin is abundant in some desert plants, betraying itself by a yellowish appearance in the epidermal cells (*Monsonia, Erodium, Astragalus, Tamarix, Linaria, Centaurea, &c.*), as well as of course by the agency of iron salts. Dr. Volkens alludes to Warming's suggestion that tannin, in connection with the hygroscopical capacity of acids, would afford a protection against dessication.[1] In alluding to this supposed use of tannin, it may be mentioned that Sachs regards it as a waste product in metabolism,[2] though fungi when attacking oakwood appear to consume it.[3]

On the other hand, Mr. S. Le M. Moore remarks that " tannic acid may have a more general relation to the turgescence of cells. Moreover, tannin is most likely used up in the lignification of the cell-wall."[4] As lignification is a prominent feature of desert plants, there may be perhaps more than a mere accidental coincidence.

[1] *Zur Flora der Ægypt.-Ar. Wüste, Skizze,* p. 14.
[2] Physiology, &c., p. 328.   [3] Sachs, *op. cit.,* p. 338.
[4] *Journ. Linn. Soc. Bot.,* xxvii. p. 538.

Another kind of secretion is that of strong-scented ethereal oils, glandular hairs being a common feature on desert plants. Species of *Artemisia* are characteristic plants of the deserts of Africa and Beluchistan; *Pulicaria arabica* has a particularly powerful odour. Since Dr. Tyndall has shown how minute quantities of such oils diffused through the air are capable of arresting radiant heat, it has been suggested that this is one of the many resources to which desert plants appeal, in order to reduce the ill effects of the heated atmosphere which surrounds them ; and, just as the presence and quantity of opium, hasheesh, aconitine, &c., secreted by plants vary greatly with the climate, so is it reasonable, in the absence of strict investigations, to assume that these oils are in an excess through the intense heat and other conditions of the climate of deserts.

Another of the more interesting secretions may be here mentioned, viz., of certain mineral salts, which by their hygrometric properties enable the plants to absorb dew from the air during the hotter months and thus transmit it to the tissues within. *Reaumuria hirtella,* species of *Tamarix, Frankenia pulverulenta,* species of *Statice* [1] and *Cressa* are the more remarkable instances. The first-named plant having developed its new foliage in early spring, when water is comparatively copious, the leaves in the early morning appear covered with dew-like drops, no doubt due to root pressure. As the sun mounts the water evaporates, and the plant is now covered with a dust-like secretion of chlorides of sodium, of calcium and of magnesium, the two latter being in less proportion than the first. There are special two-celled glands in the epidermis which secrete these salts. Later on, after the rainy period is over, these excessively hygrometric salts absorb dew, which is then transmitted to the interior of the plant, and

---

[1] See Mr. J. Wilson's paper on "Mucilage and other Glands of the Plumbagineæ." *Ann. of Bot.,* iv. 1890, p. 231.

thus enables it to retain its bright green character all through the hot season.[1]   In a similar manner a large number of very lofty *Tamarix* trees grow outside Cairo, but not quite on the desert.   They never receive any water by artificial irrigation whatever, yet are in a very flourishing condition.

Halophytic plants, and others yielding ethereal oils, though not uncommon in the Egyptian deserts, in consequence of the general presence of salts in the sand, are of course especially characteristic of more saline areas, as of the Asiatic steppes. These extensive regions agree with the more southern deserts in excessive aridity and heat, and consequently we find the same characteristic features in the plants of both alike, such as the production of spines, hairy epidermis, saline sap, and the secretion of ethereal oils.   The *Chenopodiaceæ* are especially characteristic of both regions, the salts of soda imbibed by the roots and retained within the plant rendering the water less easy of evaporation.

[1] I had a curious experience with this plant when drying it in a press for my herbarium.   Placing freshly gathered specimens in the usual way between drying papers, I proceeded to change them after three days.   To my surprise I found the sheets perfectly saturated where the specimens were lying.   They themselves were covered with dew-like drops, although under strong pressure.   The salts had, in fact, rapidly drawn out the moisture from within the plants.   After fresh papers were supplied the plant dried quickly.   There are some peculiarities in the anatomy of the leaf of *Reaumuria* which Dr. Volkens does not allude to, though he has figured the two-celled salt-glands, &c.   One is the remarkable forms which the "tracheides" of the leaves assume.   Instead of being more or less straight tubes, they bulge into bag-like processes of three or four sides, or else assume various irregular shapes.   They are thick walled, but provided with numerous small transverse slits.   They suggest the idea that they are means of temporarily storing water until it be required to be transmitted elsewhere, and would seem to support M. Vesque's view of the use of vessels or water tracheides as "reservoirs vasiformes." *

* *Op. cit.*, p. 38 (*supra*, p. 44).

Similarly there is a great secretion of ethereal oils in consequence of intense heat. Thus Grisebach observes that Arabia is on this account distinguished by its aromatic and resinous plants, of which several are equally indigenous in the steppes of the East.[1]   While, however, these environmental conditions are the direct causes of the secretion of the oils, tannin, salts, &c., these latter in their turn aid in checking the loss of water. Thus Grisebach observes :—" Les huiles éthérées paraissent également agir d'une manière restrictive à l'égard de la dépense de la vapeur aqueuse, lorsque les organes de végétation sont richement pourvus de ces éléments aromatiques.   L'huile s'évapore plus facilement que l'eau, et entoure chaque feuille d'une atmosphère imprégnée de vapeurs odoriférantes.   On sait que les vapeurs de substances différentes restent indépendantes les unes des autres dans un espace qui en est saturé, mais il n'en est pas de même lorsqu'elles sont dégagées avec rapidité des liquides, dans des conditions où il ne peut être question de saturation.   Sans doute, cette rapidité est retardée en présence d'une autre vapeur susceptible de se produire plus aisément.   C'est l'huile éthérée seule que la plante rejette comme une substance d'évacuation, tandis qu'elle doit retenir autant que possible l'eau de sa sève, lorsqu'il s'agit de prolonger la durée de ces fonctions vitales.   Un rôle de certain importance pourrait également revenir au phénomène de réfrigération produit par l'évaporation, au moment du passage rapide des huiles éthérées à l'état de vapeur, phénomène qui réagit contre la température communiquée par l'isolation aux feuilles, dont le degré de chaleur détermine aussi la marche de l'évaporation."[2]

Mount Sinai appears to show like characteristic features of desert plants to a considerable height, viz., 7035 feet; for

---

[1] *Vég. du Globe*, ii. p. 129.   [2] *Vég. du Globe*, i. p. 628.

Mr. R. M. Redhead, in some notes upon the flora, remarks :[1]
—"During our ascent of Gebel Musa, followed by that of Ras-es-Sâfsafeh, two points especially struck me, first, the great preponderance of scented and especially labiate plants ; and, secondly, the very woolly, tomentose character of those not labiated." He also speaks of "a very fragrant *Tanacetum* or *Artemisia* with pinnated downy leaves. . . . *Satureja montana* and *S. Juliana* (I think) have an odour greatly resembling the incense used by the Greek Church, and are gathered by the monks for some ecclesiastical purpose. *Salvia clandestina* has woolly pinnatifid leaves." This last-mentioned species of *Salvia* is a most variable one, and has given rise to much discussion and nomenclature. If, however, the effect of the environment be kept in view, which causes the variations, I think the passage from the European *S. Verbenaca* with large flowers and glabrous leaves to the S. European and desert forms, will be probably found to be exemplified by a gradual reduction of the leaf so as to become more deeply indented or of the "coronipifolioid" type, and by the glabrous surface passing through a pilose condition till it becomes tomentose, as described by Mr. Redhead ; while the flowers adapted to insects run through the usual degradations till they become cleistogamous. Bentham thus speaks of *S. controversa*, which *S. clandestina* connects with *S. Verbenaca* :[2]
—"It appears that in the ordinary *clandestine* state of this plant the corolla is abortive, as frequently occurs in *S. Verbenaca* and *S. clandestina*, especially in their more southern stations."

GENERAL SUMMARY OF OBSERVATIONS ON DESERT PLANTS.—
Very many additional instances might be given in illustration

[1] Notes on the Flora of the Desert of Sinai ; *Journ. Linn. Soc. Bot.*, ix. p. 208.
[2] Labiatæ, p. 719.

of each of the preceding observations; but enough has been stated to bear out the contention, first, that we are justified in concluding from innumerable coincidences between *environment* and *structure* that there is some common relation between them of cause and effect; secondly, that all parts of plants are subject to variations, and that while, on the one hand, they may be merely casual, accidental, transient, and of no classificatory value whatever, yet on the other they may become more and more persistent and characteristic, and thence hereditary, affording the systematist features which he may pronounce as varietal or specific, as the case may be. Lastly, seeing how by experimental evidence plants can lose or take on such characters according as they are grown away from or in the normal environment with which they are associated, the *cumulative evidence* amounts practically to a *demonstration* that varietal and specific characters are solely acquired through the direct action of the environment, in conjunction with the responsive powers of protoplasm.

CHAPTER IV

ORIGIN OF THE STRUCTURAL PECULIARITIES OF ALPINE AND ARCTIC PLANTS

CLIMATIC CONDITIONS OF ALPINE REGIONS.—High Alpine and Arctic regions are generally marked by well-known climatic conditions, of which aridity is perhaps the most characteristic. During the summer a very considerable temperature is acquired on the southern slopes of mountains in the Northern Hemisphere, in consequence of the rays of the sun falling in a more nearly perpendicular direction upon them. This is greatly favoured by the highly rarefied atmosphere. On the other hand, as the hot air arises from the valleys, its heat is changed into *work*, which tends to expand and so make the air more rarefied than below; while a powerful radiation, especially from snow, produces a corresponding degree of cold at night, though the light and heat may have been very pronounced during the day. Thus, for example, Drs. Hooker and Thompson, in speaking of the absence of cryptogams in the Alpine regions of the Himalaya, observe: —"This is no doubt indirectly due to the elevation of the region, and directly to the sudden accessions of great heat and drought, which are the effects of a highly rarefied atmosphere."[1] Alph. de Candolle also remarks:[2]—"La rareté de l'air dans les régions supérieures et l'action plus intense du

---

[1] *Flora Indica*, p. 101.   [2] *Géog. Bot.*, i. p. 253.

soleil augmentent, il est vrai, l'évaporation. . . . Dans les pays
tropicaux les nuages, qui stationnent à une certaine hauteur,
font que la sécheresse est infiniment plus grande au-dessus
qu'au-dessous de cette limite." M. Heckel also speaks of a
similar aridity in high latitudes as follows :—" En Scandi-
navie, l'atmosphère beaucoup moins saturée d'humidité, en
raison même de la plus basse température et action prolongée,
beaucoup plus que chez nous, de la lumière pendant toute la
saison propice à la floraison," &c.[1]

Up to the limits of the tree-line mountains are characterised by great moisture. Humid winds from below clothe
the mountains with belts of forest trees, which again themselves tend to increase the amount of moisture at the same
elevation. Above them, however, the converse conditions
obtain. The cold becomes greater as the heated air rises
from below, and then its heat disappears *as heat*, being, as
stated, converted into working energy in expanding and
rarefying the air. Evaporation and radiation consequently
become excessive, especially from snow, as Sir J. D. Hooker
says :—" Snow radiates the most powerfully of any substance
I have tried ; " and he adds, " It may account for the great
injury plants sustain from a thin covering of ice on their
foliage, even when the temperature is but little below the
freezing-point." [2]

Correlated with these environmental conditions are structural features characteristic of the plants frequenting high
altitudes. Very similar peculiarities are also characteristic
of plants growing in high latitudes ; so that the *vertical*
range of plants, as is of course well known, is comparable
with the *latitudinal* range.

---

[1] *Sur l'Intensité du Coloris et les Dimensions considérables des Fleurs aux
Hautes Altitudes ; Bull. de la Soc. Bot. de Fr.*, 1883, p. 150.

[2] *Op. cit.*, p. 410 (*supra*, p. 87).

In some respects, as in having great aridity and a powerful light, Alpine regions resemble those of deserts of low latitudes; but of course the ·temperature being so different, the effects on plant life are also very greatly different in some ways, while they agree in others.

GENERAL FEATURES OF ALPINE PLANTS.—Speaking generally, the features characteristic of Alpine plants may be enumerated as follows :—A dwarfing in size, or "nanism;" a compact habit of growth, sometimes giving a moss-like appearance and furnishing the specific terms "muscoides," &c. ; [1] a certain degree of succulency in the tissues; [2] an intenser green colour than obtains in similar plants growing in the plains at lower ·levels; an increase of hairiness on the under if not on both sides of the leaves, which may also have ciliated margins ; [3] a greater degree of hairiness may be also shared by the stems; a pubescent, villous, or tomentose condition being characteristic of certain species; with a greater brilliancy and size of the flowers, and a perennial habit of growth.

The above features are such as may be generally contrasted with those of similar or allied plants growing at lower altitudes; but it is not to be understood that all these features are to be seen together in any one plant; but *each* of them may be *often* noticed on observing Alpine plants as a whole, and that relatively more frequently than in plants generally frequenting lower situations.

[1] *E.g.*, *Veronica lycopodioides, Saxifraga bryoides*, and *S. muscoides*.

[2] *Veronica pinguifolia* of New Zealand illustrates this fact; while *Plantago alpina* is identically the same as *P. maritima*, according to Hoffman, *Untersuchen über Variation*, p. 29.

[3] The following are examples having strongly ciliated ribs or margins to the leaves :—*Papaver alpinum, Draba aizoides, Silene acaulis, Arenaria ciliata, Saxifraga androsacea, S. aspera, S. Segueri,* and other species. As instances of hairiness, see M. Battandier's observations on Algerian plants (*supra*, p. 65).

That these features should also be found, *cæteris paribus*, in Arctic plants is not strange, for several Arctic and Alpine plants are identically the same species,[1] and the latter are believed by many botanists to have survived on the summits of more southern mountains of Europe, since their dispersion from the higher latitudes after the close of the Glacial Epoch.

The climatic conditions of high altitudes and high latitudes have often been compared, the aggregate amount of heat in each during the summer being roughly comparable. But in the Arctic regions the duration of sunlight is diurnally long, the rays being very oblique ; while on the southern slopes of the Alps, at least, the heat is greater but its duration shorter. The prolongation of sunlight compensates for the lesser aggregate amount of obscure heat-rays in the Arctic regions.

The general result, therefore, accruing from the greater degree of cold in both regions, coupled with a corresponding aridity—always allowing for local exceptions—is that the average conditions of the environments become on the whole approximately alike, producing a certain amount of similarity in the *facies* of the floras.

Besides the well-recognised Alpine flora of Great Britain, which is so well known that I need not enumerate the plants, there are several which either do not belong to it or have varieties or kindred species which are Alpine ; and when this is the case these latter *assume* one or other of the normally Alpine features. Thus *Caltha palustris* is an ordinary marsh plant, but the dwarfer variety, *minor*, with solitary and smaller flowers, occurs in mountainous places. Again, *Caltha radicans*,

---

[1] For plants common to Spitzbergen and the Alps, &c., see *La Végétation du Spitzberg comparée à celle des Alpes et des Pyrénées*, par Ch. Martins, 1865.

only known in Forfarshire, is said to have been found in East
Finland. It may, therefore, be a relic of the Arctic flora.
Alchemilla arvensis is a lowland plant, but its variety *montana*
is dwarf and silky, approaching the intensely silky species
A, alpina. *Plantago maritima* is somewhat fleshy, being a
maritime plant; but it appears to be identical with *P. alpina*,
allowing for variations. *Oxyria* is also sub-fleshy.

Now, as most of if not all these features characteristic of
Alpine plants enumerated above have been proved by experiment, as will be described hereafter, to be the direct outcome
of a residence in the environmental conditions afforded by an
Alpine climate, we are quite justified in regarding the latter as
being their direct cause.

With reference to the special adaptations which they have
assumed, M. de Candolle[1] deduced the following laws as
applicable to plants growing in high altitudes as well as
latitudes.

1. "The power of each entire plant, or part of a plant, to
resist extremes of temperature bears an inverse ratio to the
quantity of water it contains." As Alpine, like desert regions,
are naturally arid to an excessive degree, the environment actually brings about the very peculiarities of the plants which
enable them to resist the difficulties of their position.

2. "The power of resisting cold [and heat] is in a direct
ratio to the viscidity of the juices which a plant contains,"
which are therefore dried up less readily if the heat be great
as in the deserts. "This may be one reason why resinous
trees, such as some of the *Coniferæ*, are found to brave so well
the cold of the most northern latitudes, and likewise that
of the highest mountains of the globe." The resinous secretions of the *Pinaceæ* are, however, the actual outcome of the

---

[1] Quoted by Daubeney, "On Climate," p. 77.

dry climatal conditions under which they thrive. Conversely, Sir J. D. Hooker remarks on the absence of many useful pines at a high elevation near the Tibetan frontier, where they might à priori be expected, if it were not for the *humidity;* for he says that *Abies Brunoniana* and *A. Smithiana* growing at Lamteng fail to produce any quantity of resin, turpentine, or pitch, a fact " which may perhaps be accounted for by the humidity of the climate." [1]

3. " The resistance to cold in a plant is in the inverse ratio to the mobility of its juices, just as we find that water may be cooled several degrees below the freezing-point without passing into a state of ice, if only kept undisturbed."

4. " The larger the diameter of the vessels and cells in a plant may be, the more liable it is to injury from frost; just as we find that water becomes solid much sooner in wide than it does in capillary tubes." Perhaps the absence of vessels in the *Pinaceæ* is correlated with this law.

5. " The power of resisting extremes of temperature bears a direct ratio to the quantity of air entangled between the parts of the vegetable tissue."

" The down which covers the exterior of certain organs in many plants [is] a protection against both excessive heat [as in the deserts] and excessive cold [which results from radiation in the high Alpine regions], in consequence of the air contained within its meshes, which serves to prevent the rapid transmission of heat either from without or from within."

The point, then, which I maintain is that the excessive aridity, the brilliancy of sunlight, and the great cold arising from radiation are the actual *causes* which have brought about all the peculiarities of anatomical details which characterise

---

[1] Him. Journ., Minerva edit., p. 318.

high Alpine vegetation; and that these structures themselves render Alpine plants best fitted to survive, being in direct adaptation to their environment.

I will now consider special peculiarities of Alpine plants.

NANISM.—The dwarfing of ligneous plants, such as willows, birches, beeches, firs, &c., whether on high mountains of both worlds or in Arctic and Antarctic regions, is too well known to be emphasised here; but the same rule applies to shrubs and herbaceous plants. Thus, in Coulter's manual of the Botany of the Rocky Mountains, as Mr. Cockerell observes,[1] "Thirty-nine varieties are described which are peculiar in part at least for their dwarfed stature;" and he adds, "that such dwarfing is the result of external conditions can hardly be disputed." Of herbaceous plants he remarks:—"Phlox is a genus of fine herbaceous plants; Silene in its usual forms is not insignificant in size; but on the summit of the Colorado Mountains we get *species* of these genera, *Phlox cæspitosa* and *Silene acaulis*, so dwarfed and densely matted on the ground that people call them 'flowering mosses.' Here clearly the dwarfing has become permanent and peculiar to the species."

M. Th. Rittener has some interesting observations on species of Gentian. He describes,[2] under the name of *G. Favrati*, a variety of *G. verna*, differentiated from the type by the divisions of the corolla being larger, by *the stem being shorter*, and especially by its rounded leaves, which are much smaller. This variety, "produced by altitude and exposure," as he observes, is the last term of diminution of the type. .

---

[1] *Nature Notes*, vol. v. p. 15; and *Nature*, vol. xliii. p. 207, where Mr. Cockerell needlessly suggests that "natural selection may come into play."

[2] *Gentiana verna*, L.; M. Th. Rittener, *Bull. Soc. Vaud. Sci. Nat.*, xxii. p. 95, 1886 (Lausanne), with plates giving comparative drawings of *G. Favrati*, *G. brachyphylla*, Froel., *G. Verna*, L., *G. angulosa*, Bisb., and *G. imbricata*, Schl.

Mr. P. Sewell also speaks of plants growing at an elevation of 7000 feet on the Maritime Alps as being "curiously dwarfed."[1]

The "muscoidal" or moss-like feature of many Alpine plants is not unfamiliar to explorers of our own mountains, such as *Arenaria Cherleri*, Benth. (*Cherleria sedoides*, L.); *Sagina Linnæi*, subsp. *nivalis; Silene acaulis*, L., called "Moss Campion" in Scotland; similarly *Saxifraga hypnoides* and its varieties, as well as *S. aizoides*, &c. : but such forms of plants are developed more or less on all mountains of considerable height. For example, Signor Bolos writes me as follows from Spain :—" Many species which grow in our valleys and on the Pyrenean Sierras (Alpine regions) present in their places dwarf forms so distinct from the original type that they appear to be different plants or varieties, such, *e.g.*, as *Cardamine amara, Erysimum ochreleucum, Aquilegia vulgaris.* This last is also very viscous."

Sir J. D. Hooker writes :—" On the top of these hills (of the Palung Plateau), which, for barrenness, reminded me of the descriptions given of the Siberian steppes, I found, at 17,000 feet elevation, several minute Arctic plants, with *Rhododendron nivale*, the most Alpine of woody plants. On their sterile slopes grew a curious plant allied to the *Cherleria* of the Scotch Alps, forming great hemispherical balls on the ground, eight to ten inches across, altogether resembling in habit the curious Balsam-bog, *Bolax glebaria*, of the Falkland Islands, which grows in very similar scenes."[2]

Dr. Aitchison describes similar hummock-like forms at elevations from 3000 to 5000 feet, in Afghanistan, "similar to the peculiar South American genus *Bolax*, which vary from the size of a football to small mounds twelve feet across

---

[1] *Trans. and Proc. Bot. Soc. Edin.*, 1890, p. 383.

[2] Him. Journ., p. 351.

and five feet high. The plants taking this form are usually
species of *Acanthophyllum* belonging to *Caryophylleæ*, *Astragalus* and *Onobrychis* among *Leguminosæ*, and *Acantholimon*
and *Statice* of *Plumbagineæ.*"[1]   At an elevation of 5000 feet
he speaks of "a very moss-like primulaceous plant, *Dionysia
tapetodes.*[2]

MM. Bureau and Franchet describe a number of dwarf
plants from Tibet; for the flora of the region where they
were collected is marked by the stunted form of the shrubs
and dwarf character of the herbaceous vegetation.   "It is
characteristically a vegetation of high peaks, where drought
and strong winds are the main climatic features.   The *Papa-
veraceæ* are represented especially by dwarf, large-flowered
kinds of *Meconopsis*.   The greater number of the species of
Corydalis are not more than two or three inches high.   The
Cruciferæ, such as *Parrya ciliaris*, in the same way are dwarf
and large-flowered.   *Silene cæspitosa* may be compared with
the most dwarf states of *S. acaulis* of our own high mountains.
The honeysuckle of Tibet constitutes only a small bush about
a foot high, with intertangled branches.   But it is especially
in the Rhododendrons and Primulas that this dwarf character
is remarkable.   All the Rhododendrons and Primulas found
between Lhassa and Sitang—*R. principis*, *R. primulæflorum*,
R. nigropunctatum, *Primula leptopoda*, *P. diantha*, and *P.
Henrici*—may be ranged among the dwarfest types of the
genera to which they belong.   It is the same with *Incar-
villea*.   The Tibetan species belong to a group found also

---

[1] *Op. cit.*, p. 431 (*supra*, p. 37).

[2] *Ibid.*, p. 427.   For a good illustration of two species of the genus
Haastia, which assumes this quaint form, the reader may be referred to
"The Natural History of Plants," by Kerner and Oliver, p. 188, fig. 253,
where a scene in New Zealand is given with *H. pulvinaris* and *H. Sinclairii*,
the so-called "vegetable sheep," represented as growing upon the rocks.

in Kansu and Central Yunnan, with stems almost obliterated and corollas very large." [1]

In the Southern Hemisphere there is the familiar *Nertera depressa* of cultivated plants, and if we travel further south-wards we should find *Drapetes muscosa* (*Thymelaceæ*) occurring in Kernite Island and the mountains of Antarctic America; *Bolax glebaria*, alluded to above, which forms hemispherical balls on rocky clay-slate in the Falkland Islands; *Azorella Selago*, the most abundant plant in Kerguelen's Island; and the unique *Lyallia Kerguelensis* also on Kerguelen's Island. Lastly, *Goudotia tolimensis* represents a Hepatica.[2]

Such are a few of the innumerable instances of nanism which applies to trees, shrubs, and flowering herbs of all kinds which are capable of living in high Alpine regions and in high latitudes, Arctic and Antarctic.

Causes of Nanism.—Though the general or perhaps the chief cause of nanism on mountains and high latitudes is un-doubtedly a low temperature and aridity of the atmosphere [3] which checks growth, it must be noted that any cause which has this effect may bring it about, and if persisted in for many generations begets a varietal or specific type. Thus on our chalk downs the soil is often only a few inches in depth, and the plants are to a large extent more or less dwarfed. Consequently, some are recognised as sub-species if not species by systematists; as, *e.g.*, *Cnicus acaulis*, which, however, readily produces its stem in a rich soil, and when growing among other plants of some height; *Erythræa Centaurium*, sub-species *capitata*, growing on the Downs of Sussex and the Isle of Wight, with a short stem; similarly, the "stunted" character of *Polygala calcarea* is probably due to the dry soil

---

[1] From *Nature*, vol. xliv. p. 260.
[2] *Ann. des Sci. Nat.*, Sér. 3, tom. iv. 1845, pl. 4.
[3] See De Candolle, *Géog. Bot.*, i. p. 310.

in which it grows, &c. It is quite conceivable that a poor soil may often contribute to the production of nanism and "starved" forms which become perpetuated, as of *Poa rigida*, and "depauperated" conditions, which, indeed, often supply the specific name "depauperata."

A further result arises from the impoverishment of the seeds. Thus M. A. Roujon[1] selected the smallest seeds from the least developed specimens of *Helianthus annuus*, of *Calendula arvensis*, and *Zea mais*. In two years he obtained very diminutive plants. Of these, maize was reduced in size to 20 cms., while *Calendula arvensis* resembled *Cicendia filiformis*, and bore one flower only. While the height diminished, the number of seeds decreased, the ultimate result being absolute sterility.[2] Such, however, is by no means always the case;[3] for although Vilmorin possessed a sterile dwarf, *Ageratum cœruleum*, which could only be propagated by the vegetative system, another plant proved to be very fertile and fixed in character. M. Verlot,[4] who mentions this fact, says that dwarf races of cultivated plants possess the faculty of reproduction in a high degree. He observes that nanism is commoner with cultivated plants than in wild conditions, and that but few kinds of plants have not sooner or later produced dwarf varieties, such as the French bean and scarlet runner, &c. He adds that both Lamarck and Linnæus noticed that poor silicious soils, as well as dry and arid ones, predispose

---

[1] *De quelques Variations considérables observées chez les Végétaux. Journ. d'Hist. Nat. de Bordeaux et du Sud-Ouest*, tom. iii. p. 156, 1884.

[2] My own experiments have already been referred to (*supra*, p. 6).

[3] I have repeated these experiments with other plants, and have raised a crop of candytuft for four years, of about three inches in height, by selecting the smallest seeds. It requires further testing, for in the present year (1894) several individuals have recovered their normal height, others remaining dwarf.

[4] *Sur la Production et la Fixation des Variétés, &c.*, 1865.

plants to nanism, This I have myself observed in Egypt.
Thus I found plants of *Ranunculus sceleratus* growing near
the Great Pyramid only two inches in height. *Juncus bufonius*
forms little tufts scarcely an inch in height among the rocks
in Malta ; and *Calendula ægyptiaca*, which attains to a height
of two or three feet in the cultivated Nile-land, is only a few
inches in height in the desert. Mr. Cockerel, who studied the
plants of the Rocky Mountains, attributes the hereditary character of nanism to impoverishment.[1]

Some, if not all, of such dwarf wild-flowers would probably
regain a corresponding vigour 'and much greater height if
grown in a richer soil. Such cases, therefore, will not apply
to dwarfs arising in the usual conditions of cultivation in a
rich and prepared soil.

Though so many dwarf varieties appear under the hands
of horticulturists, and, if desired, can be carefully selected
and propagated till their nanism is fixed, the cultivators, as
a rule, can give no account of the *causes* which first produce
this character. M. Verlot, however, found that he could
almost raise them at will among many annuals—in which
dwarfs mostly occur—*by sowing the seed late in the season*,
from August to September, and by successive "pricking" out
of the seedlings. The following is his own account of the
procedure : [2]—"Prenons pour exemple le *Calliopsis tinctoria*.
Après l'avoir semé en août-septembre, nous devrons, dans une
culture bien entendue, dès qu'il aura développé quelques
feuilles, le repiquer dans une pépinière d'attente, en laissant
entre les plantes un espace suffisant pour qu'ils puissent croître
librement. Lorsque les feuilles viendront à se toucher, nous
devrons nécessairement opérer un nouveau repiquage, que nous

---

[1] *Nature*, vol. xliii. p. 207.
[2] *Sur la Production et la Fixation des Variétés dans les Plantes d'orne-ment*, 1865, p. 40.

renouvellerons une troisième et peut-être même une quatrième fois ; après quoi nous les mettrons en place. , Or, qu'aurons-nous obtenu par ces repiquages successifs ? Des plantes fortes, vigoureuses, fermes, trapues ; nous aurons favorisé le développement des ramifications inférieures qui se sera nécessairement opéré au détriment de celui de la tige principale, et nous aurons ainsi créé un individu comparativement nain. Si maintenant nous récoltons des graines sur les plantes ainsi cultivées, et que nous donnions les mêmes soins aux individus qui en naîtront, nous obtiendrons, d'année en année, des êtres chez lesquels on aura fait développer une certaine tendance au nanisme. En un mot, des graines recueillies sur des plantes ainsi traitées pendant plusieurs générations seront plus aptes que d'autres à produire des variétés naines, et cela est tellement vrai que la plupart de ces variétés appartiennent à des plantes qu'on peut semer à l'automne, ou bien à celles qui, semées au printemps, sont soumises à des repiquages successifs. Ainsi, parmi les espèces annuelles qu'on sème habituellement de juillet en septembre, les suivantes ont produit les variétés naines :—*Calceolaria plantaginea, Senecio cruentus, Agrostemma Cœli-Rosa, Calliopsis tinctoria, Œnothera Drummondii, Helichrysum bracteatum, Leptosiphon densiflorum, Dianthus sinensis, Scabiosa atropurpurea, Schizanthus retusus, Iberis umbellata.*

"Et parmi celles qu'on sème au printemps, et dont les plantes sont soumises à des repiquages successifs, nous citerons les suivantes : *Impatiens Balsamina, Callistephus sinensis, Tagetes patula, T. erecta, T. signata.*"

It may perhaps be suggested that it was due to a similar cause, in the case of the autumn-sown plants, to that which produces Alpine nanism, namely, a reduction of temperature and a checked vitality; because when M. Bonnier grew *Helianthus tuberosus* at high elevations, it did not form its customary tall central stem, but a rosette of leaves only on the ground. Similarly by sowing plants late in the season, the temperature becomes similarly insufficient to develop the main axis: even the successive pricking out, by repeatedly checking growth, may have had something to do with it.

An analogous circumstance is seen in checking the reproductive energy in the origin of the garden carrot, as raised by M. Vilmorin; who, by sowing the seed of the wild annual plant in autumn, succeeded in fixing the habit of flowering in the second season, thereby converting it into a biennial.

As another and quite distinct cause of nanism is by pollination, M. Verlot writes :—"Un fait curieux, dont nous devons la communication à l'obligeance de M. Mac-Nab, démontrerait cependant qu'étant opérée d'une certaine manière, la fécondation pourrait produire des individus ayant une tendance au nanisme. . . . 'Il est une circonstance qu'on a récemment fait connaître,' dit M. Mac-Nab, 'et sur le résultat de laquelle on ne doit avoir aucun doute : c'est que les meilleures variétés naines de *Rhododendron* sont celles obtenues par l'emploi du pollen pris sur les petites étamines. Les produits qu'on en obtient, je puis le certifier, sont très différents de ceux obtenus par l'emploi du pollen des grandes étamines.'"[1]

M. Bonnier, in a later and more elaborate account,[2] figures and describes the appearance of several species of plants which he grew both at a low and a high altitude respectively. The latter were dwarfed and much more hairy. *Helianthus tuberosus* formed nothing but a rosette of very shaggy leaves on the

---

[1] Verlot, *op. cit.*, p. 42. See also Darwin's reference to Naudin's experiments (*Nouvelles Archives du Muséum*, tom. i. p. 27) in raising dwarf and impoverished plants by fertilising with only a few grains of pollen. "Animals and Plants," &c., ii. 369.

[2] *Revue Gén. de Bot.*, tom. ii. p. 513. See also *Comptes Rendus*, cxl. 1890, p. 363 ; tom. cxi. 377.

ground; while *Achemilla vulgaris, Lotus corniculatus,* and
Potentilla Tormentilla formed prostrate instead of erect
flowering stems. This arrest of the main stem with a production of a rosette of radical leaves is a common mountainous
feature. Mr. Scott Elliott[1] found it to be so in the South
African Mountains. He says:—"I have often noticed that
the commonest form of the plants growing on the summits
is quite different from that found lower down. Perhaps it
is best described as the Hieracium type. It is distinguished
by having crowded radical leaves. It is strikingly absent
on the lower slopes except in moist places.[2]

The prostrate habit mentioned above is also characteristic
of many Alpine plants. This is well seen in the creeping
willows, &c., at high altitudes in Switzerland. Dr. J. A.
Henriques, of the Botanic Gardens, Coimbra, tells me that
Juniperus nana modifies itself in a similar manner on the
Sierra da Estrella, the highest mountain in Portugal: "Dans
les régions élevées (1900 m.) tous les rameaux sont tout a fait
farcis et la plante s'accole aux rochers, et tout ça sans doute
à cause de la neige que la recouvre pendant quelques mois."

So Dr. D. Mariano de la Paz Graells observes in a letter
to me:—"The low temperature of the soil and air of such
[Alpine] regions acts by restraining the expansive forces of
the organism, which thus tends more and more to contract
than to expand; hence the reason why living creatures when
subjected to the like influences become dwarfed at high
elevations, though when the same species is removed to
a lower zone it acquires larger proportions. Such is the case
with *Juniperus Sabina, J. vulgaris,* and *J. arborescens, J.*

---

[1] *Op. cit. (supra,* p. 46).

[2] For further literature on this subject, the reader may be referred to
Prince Kropotkin's "Recent Science," *Nineteenth Century,* April 1894,
p. 688.

pyramidata, and the variety *humilis,* which is prostrate, forming rounded and very dense tufts. It has consequently been called the 'creeping Sabina.' *J. nana,* also called *alpina,* which is neither more nor less than *J. communis,* L., sends out from the very 'collar of the root' long branches trailing on the ground, as is generally the case with perennial Alpine plants."

As another illustration Mr. D. Dewar of the Botanic Gardens, Glasgow, has kindly communicated to me the following:—"*Arabis anachortica,* a species . found in cave-like situations in the Alps, and on account of which it has very thin papery leaves, was introduced to Kew. In three generations raised from seed we turned it into *A. alpina.* Similarly *Geum montanum* is a low-growing, one-flowered species on the mountain tops; but when it occurs lower down and under the influence of the rich wash from the cowsheds, it grows three times larger, with a branching, many-flowered stem, and bears much larger flowers. *Geum Chiloense* affords similar changes. *G. C. grandiflorum* is simply the result of cultivation, a most marked instance of variation under new conditions."

That a warmer temperature of the air than that of the soil is the main cause in the production of an erect stem at low altitudes, and conversely a prostrate one at higher elevations, seems to be probable from the following additional considerations. In the summer of 1889, which was a warm one, the stems of M. Bonnier's experimental plants increased in height; while they were checked in growth when a lower temperature prevailed in consequence of the surrounding air being insufficiently heated in the rarefied atmosphere of high Alpine regions.·

On the other hand, the temperature of the soil is higher under those conditions than that of the air immediately above it, so that *thermotropism* may, I think, be suggested, in the absence of sufficient experimental evidence, as the direct cause of the shoots produced at the base lying along the ground.

The following analogy will, I think, tend to corroborate this probability. When plants are grown in total darkness, as potatoes, &c., there being nothing but a sufficient heat to induce growth, the stems are abnormally elongated, and of course white and leafless; secondly, if plants are grown under coloured glasses, I find, *cœteris paribus*, that the stems become increasingly elongated under green, yellow, and red glasses respectively, corresponding to a relatively increased amount of calorific rays with a diminution of the total amount of luminous and more refracted rays of the spectrum.

As another example, ivy when it has climbed to the top of a wall, instead of growing erect into the air above it, grows at right angles to the previous portion of the stem, *i.e.*, along the horizontal surface of the top. As this is equally illuminated with the vertical surface, there could be no other conceivable difference on *à priori* grounds except temperature, the top of the wall being presumably warmer than the air immediately above it. The ivy will there grow either towards the sun or away from it.

From the above and many other similar facts it would seem that we have sufficient grounds for concluding that the temperature of the air surrounding the plants is insufficient for producing an erect axial development in Alpine situations. It would seem, therefore, that we must look to *the differences in temperature* between that of *the soil* and that of *the air* above it. If the latter be relatively colder and the former relatively warmer, a prostrate habit may result. If the air, however, be very warm, an elongation of the stem may be expected, especially if the amount of light be reduced.

M. de Candolle observed that the soil is warmer than the
air in high altitudes,.for he says : [1]—"Les brouillards stationnent sur les hauteurs surtout pendant la nuit ; les sommités
sont souvent dégarnies de nuages aux heures les plus chaudes
de la journée ; enfin la neige les empêche dans beaucoup
de cas de se refroidir pendant l'hiver.   Il en résulte que
la couche superficielle du sol doit en général être plus chaude
sur les montagnes que dans la plaine, la moyenne extérieure
étant supposée semblable. M. Ch. Martins a constaté, au
sommet du Faulhorn, une température moyenne du sol bien
supérieure à celle de l'air" (Séries Météor. au Sommet du
Faulhorn).[2]

Not only is it the case in high altitudes and high latitudes
as well, but. the same interpretation would seem to account
for decumbent and prostrate stems in other localities, characters which are often regarded as specific.   Thus I noticed
in Malta, which is remarkable for its rocky character, that
very many plants growing exposed were prostrate, the leaves
spreading out in close contact with the ground, or if growing
in crevices in the limestone rocks, the leaves were closely
adpressed against the surface.   When dug up, the leaves would
become still more reflexed and press themselves down against
the tap-root, as, *e.g.*, *Taraxicum officinale*, var. *minimum*, showing how strong the epinastic tendency was.   *Malva sylvestris*
assumes two well-marked forms.   When it grows, but very
rarely so in Malta, among other plants in loose rubble or
deeper soil, it is erect, growing to a height of two, three, or
more feet ; but it is almost invariably to be seen by hard road-

---

[1] *Géog. Bot.*, i. p. 260.

[2] Kerner and Oliver give a pretty illustration of prostrate and dwarf
Alpine plants, as well as a table showing the excess of the mean tempera-
ture of the soil above that of the air in the Central Tyrolese Alps.
"Natural History of Plants," i. p. 524 *seq.*

sides in Malta, with a very slight depth of soil over the rock. In this condition it is perfectly prostrate, sending out its numerous branches in close contact with the ground.[1] *Malva parviflora* has exactly the same habit, both in Malta and on hardened soil about Cairo; but when it is cultivated in fields in Egypt as a pot-herb, it then sends up erect stems, the tendency to "prostration" being very much reduced.

As another Maltese illustration, the cultivated "clover," *Hedysarum coronarium*, grows in the fields to a height of three or more feet, while stray plants may occasionally be seen by the roadsides. These are then as prostrate as the mallows.

Bluebells may be often observed in early spring in England with their first formed leaves pressed upon the ground, while plantains always have them in this condition when growing in a closely cut turf. They are much more erect in loose grass by roadsides.

The following observations on temperatures will perhaps show how thermotropism may account for the prostrate position of the leaves of certain plants.

The temperature on the surface of the damp soil by the side of a bluebell, growing in the shade of trees, at 9.45 A.M., 15th April 1891, a sunless morning, was 47° F. The temperature of the air three inches above the ground at the same spot was 44.5°. At 4 P.M. of the same day, on the surface of the soil the temperature was 60°. That of the air 3 inches above it was 52°.

On a tennis-lawn, the grass being covered with dew, on the same morning the temperature was 52.5°. At 4.30 P.M. of the same day, the temperature on the grass in shade was 59°. Three inches above it, it was 55°.

The temperature of the grass exposed to the sun on the same

---

[1] I have observed the same features in England, but less frequently.

day and hour was 60°; three inches above it, the temperature of the air was 58°.

On a dry surface of a flower-bed, which was damp immediately below, the temperature was 62°. That of the air 3 inches above it was 54°.

These examples will show that during the daytime in early spring the temperature of the ground was higher than that of the air immediately above it; and as light is one of the most important agents for exciting the energies of protoplasm, so too thermotropism is probably also most active during the day in causing leaves and stems to lie flat upon the surfaces around them. It may thus account for the several plants assuming a prostrate habit at high altitudes when M. Bonnier grew them there, which are usually erect at lower elevations where a warmer air temperature obtains.

Lastly, these various habits are used by systematists as classificatory characters, because they are tolerably constant under the conditions in which the plants are usually collected.

CHAPTER V

CHARACTERISTIC FEATURES OF ALPINE AND ARCTIC PLANTS
(continued)

FOLIAGE OF HIGH ALPINE PLANTS.—The tendency to reduce the size of the leaves of plants in very high altitudes and latitudes is in many plants so marked as to become a representative feature; and when precisely similar results obtain in plants of widely dissimilar orders, but are associated with an excessively dry atmosphere, one cannot but be compelled to assume that a like cause has produced a like effect. As illustrative of this fact, the Alpine Veronicas of New Zealand mountains are quite comparable with members of the Cupressineæ of California and Japan; while *Tamarix* and *Salsola Pachoi* of the African desert have precisely similarly adpressed diminutive leaves.[1]

A brief account of a few selected species of Veronica will not be out of place. Not only do they pass from strong growing bushes in the lowlands with large coriaceous leaves to dwarf shrubs, and even moss-like carpetings at high altitudes, but the leaves become smaller and smaller till they assume the closely adpressed form typical of *Thuja, Retinospora, Cupressus,* &c.

When they have become "degraded" to this stage, they may throw out the "earlier" more spinescent (or else the

---

[1] See *supra*, p. 48.

cut-leaved) form, and become dimorphic, precisely as is the case with *Cupressineæ* and *Tamariscineæ*.

The following species will illustrate these observations. Commencing with the small-leaved form *V. buxifolia*, the foliage of which resembles that of our box, as the name implies; it grows on the mountains of Canterbury Province. The next in ascending series is *V. tetragona*, reaching to an altitude of 3000 feet. *V. cupressoides* forms bushes five to six feet high up to 4000 feet, but becomes a dwarf plant only one foot high at 5500 feet. Similarly *V. Pimeloides* becomes reduced in size from two feet to ten inches in rising from 1000 to 4000 feet. At 5000 feet *V. tetrasticha* is met with as well as *V. pinguifolia*, ranging from 2500 to 5000 feet, together with the probably ancestral form of *Veronica*, viz., *Pygmæa ciliolata*, having five petals but only two stamens; this assumes a "muscoidal" form, while *P. pulvinaris* makes a carpet-like covering on the ground at 6000 feet. Again, at 5500 feet the sub-fleshy *V. salicornoides* and the dwarf form of *V. cupressoides* are met with. At 7500 feet *V. Buchanani* forms straggling shrubs, its range extending from 3000 to 7500 feet. Lastly, at 8000 feet *V. Hectori* is to be seen on the mountains of Otago, forming spreading patches six to eight inches high, and dimorphic as the other species. It is associated with *V. Lycopodioides*.

It will be thus seen that the genus *Veronica* furnishes exactly parallel features with other genera of plants in mountainous situations, and that under similar climatic and other conditions we always find closely representative types of foliage, so that botanists at once apply specific names indicating the similarities. All I contend for, therefore, is, that such forms are due to precisely the same causes; the same or homologous organs put on precisely the same morphological features in response to the similar and direct actions of a like environment: so that all these species have arisen without any aid from natural selection whatever.

PILOSISM OF ALPINE PLANTS.—The peculiarity of hairiness is often pronounced in certain species, so that many observers of Alpine plants have noticed it; and it may be remembered that pilosism is particularly noticeable in plants growing in any very dry situation as compared with aquatic species and denizens of marshes in our temperate climates. Thus, for example, Sir J. D. Hooker describes "large silky cushions of a Forget-me-not growing among the rocks" in Sikkim.[1] Elsewhere he alludes to a strong-scented silky wormwood and a woolly *Leontopodium*.[2] The common English species of our fields, *Myosotis arvensis*, is very rough, with spreading hairs; but in the true Forget-me-not, the aquatic *M. palustris*, and the sub-aquatic *M. cæspitosa*, they are scanty and adpressed.[3]

Linnæus mentions how *Myosotis* varies in this respect:— "Myosotidis foliis hirsutis et glabris varietates, apud Casp. Bauhinum aliosque enatæ sunt."[4] When we look for a general cause it appears to be the same as elsewhere, viz., the aridity of the atmosphere as well as perhaps an insufficient supply of moisture in the soil; for aridity, as already stated, tends to check the development of the parenchymatous tissues, while this causes a diversion of energy, so to say, which finds vent in pilosism.[5]

---

[1] *Op. cit.*, p. 355 (*supra*, p. 92).   [2] *Op. cit.*, p. 406, note.

[3] I find this variation in the direction of the hairs is *to some extent* correlated to a dry and moist atmosphere. Thus, *e.g.*, on the runners of *Ranunculus repens* the hairs may lie in either direction, parallel or perpendicular to the axis. They are somewhat peculiar. The basal part is bent like a "hockey" stick, the lumen being contracted at the head; the base of the hair being, so to say, banked up by rounded cells on one side.

[4] *Philos. Bot.*, p. 247, § 316.

[5] See *supra*, p. 59 *seq.*, for a discussion on this subject.

Professor Eug. Warming, in describing the plants of Lagoa Santa (Brésil),[1] observes:—"En réalité, rien n'est plus rare dans les Campos de Lagoa Santa qu'un végétal vraiment vert. . . . En 1865, Netto attribuait déjà au refroidissement que subissent les plantes des plateaux élevés du Brésil ce développement exceptionnel des poils sur tous les organes aériens."

In both cases the *cause* of pilosism appears to be due to a check to growth, in the deserts by heat, in Alpine and Arctic regions by cold.

That pilosism is a direct result of climatic conditions is obvious from experimental evidence; for it appeared as soon as plants brought from lower altitudes were grown at much higher ones; and conversely the hairiness at once decreased when they were brought down and cultivated at lower levels. M. Battandier discovered this to be the case in the observation I have already had occasion to quote in reference to the hairiness of desert plants.[2] He remarks that pilosism is very general upon all the French mountains; and M. Bonnier, who grew a number of plants taken from the plains to high altitudes, found that many "became very hairy;" *Helianthus tuberosus*, for instance, developed even "very shaggy" leaves. Similarly in the Pyrenees, Sign. Bolos writes me from Spain about *Lavatera maritima*:— "Between the variety which grows on the littoral zone and that which grows at St. Andiol de Viga (Eastern Pyrenees— height, 600 metres) the difference is so great that the latter has been classified as *incana*. It is very hairy, while its stalks are very robust and corrugated."

On the other hand, Sir J. D. Hooker found that it was

---

[1] *Op. cit.*, p. 155 (*supra*, p. 2).

[2] *Note sur des Cultures comparées des mêmes Espèces à diverses Altitudes. Bull. de la Soc. Bot. de Fr.*, 1886, p. 467.

exceptional on certain high altitudes on one of the passes of Tibet. He describes, indeed, *Saussurea gossypina* as forming "great clubs of the softest white wool, six inches to a foot high, its flowers and leaves seeming uniformly clothed with the warmest fur that nature can devise." This reminds one of the *Edelweiss, Gnaphalium leontopodium* of the Swiss Alps. "Generally speaking," he adds, "the Alpine plants of the Himalaya are quite unprovided with any special protection of this kind; it is the prevalence and conspicuous nature of the exceptions that mislead, and induce the careless observer to generalise hastily from solitary instances; for the prevailing Alpine genera of the Himalaya, Arenarias, Primroses, Saxifrages, Fumitories, Ranunculi, Gentians, Grasses, Sedges, &c., have almost uniformly naked foliage." [1]

With reference to the acquirement of hair by fleshy-leaved plants when growing at high altitudes, Dr. D. Mariano de la Paz Graells observes that some do not change, while others do. He thus writes :—"With regard to the thick-leaved plants which I have seen growing spontaneously on the Mediterranean coast, among them being *Mesembryanthemum abbreviatum, Cactus Opuntia, Aloë vulgaris, Agave Americana,* when they have been removed to the central table-land of Spain, even to the height of 1000 metres, in spite of this elevation and of the winters' frosts and snows, I have never observed their leaves to develop any hairiness. They continue fleshy, succulent, hairless, and smooth. On the other hand, hairiness will present itself on the thick-leaved plants of Pyrenean and Alpine regions; for I have frequently found in the snowy and frosty regions of the Sierra de Gredos, *Sedum Hispanicum,* [2]

---

[1] *Op. cit.*, p. 156 (*supra*, p. 92).

[2] *S. Hispanicum* is described in De Cand., Prod. iii. 406, "*foliis glaucis;*" so that it appears to become hairy like the normally Alpine species *S. hirsutum.*

S. villosum, and *S. hirsutum*, which wear their tomentose raiment, as well as *Pictoricia Hispanica*, D. C., so common on the sandy plains of both Castiles."

PSEUDO-SPECIES OF BOTANISTS.—Dr. D. Mariano de la Paz Graells, in the interesting letter from which I have just quoted, adds the following remarks upon some of the many so-called species, which he shows are only modifications due to the environment. Thus of *Pyrethrum sulphureum* and *Dianthus brachyanthus* he writes :—"The polymorphism which these plants acquire at different elevations has given rise to the formation of distinct species, *i.e.*, admitted as such by botanists of note. Studying the original division of *P. pulverulentum* of Lagasca and of *P. sulphureum* of Boissier and Renter, Willkon has united them into one single species, which he has called in his *Prodromus Flora Hispanica, P. Hispanicum*. In this he recognises two well-defined groups, the 'pinnatifid' and 'laciniate' types, placing in the first group *P. pulverulentum* of Lagasca and the *P. radicans* of Cavanilles; and in the second, *P. sulphureum*, Boiss. et Rent., which Asio had named *Chrysanthemum Aragonense*, and *C. Bocconi* or *P. Bocconi*, Wal., *P. versicolor*, Willkon; which turns out to be the *P. sulphureum*, var. *P. alpinum*, Boiss. et Rent.

"The same thing has happened with *Dianthus brachyanthus*, Boiss. et Rent., which Xatar and Maill took to be *D. attenuatus*, Benth., in the Pyrenees, and Koch for *D. virgineus;* such mistakes being due to the modifications produced by varying elevations. In some cases the very same organs become atrophied or disappear, while in others they become much more developed than usual."

EXPERIMENTAL EVIDENCE OF THE EFFECT OF THE EXTERNAL CONDITIONS OF HIGH ALTITUDES UPON PLANTS.—We are indebted to MM. Bonnier and Flahault[1] and others for interesting papers on the effects upon plants grown at high altitudes and latitudes when compared with those upon the same species, or even upon *half* of one and the same identical plant, when grown at Paris or lower altitudes and latitudes.

As an example, *Teucrium Scorodonia*, sown at a high situation above the Col d'Aspin in the Pyrenees, produced aërial stems which were very short, with leaves relatively darker green, with more abundant hairs, and an inflorescence more compact and bearing at the base very short internodes.

On the contrary, seeds gathered from individuals of the same species growing at higher altitudes than it can reach in the Pyrenees (1700 m.), and sown at Paris, produced at the end of three years elongated stems, less abundant hairs and brighter green leaves, the internodes being more elongated and more numerous.

These latter plants of *Teucrium* were nearly comparable in general aspect to those from like sowings made in the same soil from seeds obtained in the neighbourhood of Paris.

As another case, M. Bonnier found that *Lotus corniculatus* and *L. uliginosus* change very materially. He obtained different individuals of *L. corniculatus* which differed from each other more than these two species. Describing the anatomy, he observes that in cutting the pedicel below the ripe fruit, one sees that the arrangement of the cortex, the structure of the pericycle and of the cords, as well as the thickening of the epidermis, vary considerably. Thus plants of *Lotus corniculatus* from Alpine situations show an epidermis which is very thick,

---

[1] *Nouvelles Observations sur les Modifications des Végétaux suivant les Conditions Physiques du Milieu*, par M. C. L. Flahault. *Ann. des Sci. Nat. Bot.*, 1879, p. 159; *Bull. de la Soc. Bot. de Fr.*, 1886, p. 467; *Rev. Gén. de Bot.*, ii. 1891, p. 513.

a collenchymatous cortex, a pericycle without large and special cells, and the wood relatively reduced; while in certain plants of *L. corniculatus* and *L. uliginosus*, cultivated in lower altitudes, the epidermis is not so thick, the cortex is without collenchyma, the pericycle has here and there special cells, and the wood is relatively more developed.

Another observer, Herr K. Leist,[1] compares the foliage of Alpine plants with similar ones in low lands, and gives the following as the results of his observations. (1) There is a diminished thickness but an increased extent of surface to the leaf. The former is due to a decreased development of the palisade tissue, by either a reduction in the number of layers, or by a decrease in the vertical diameters of the cells, corresponding to an increase in their width, the numbers of layers being the same. The number and size of the intercellular spaces are increased, the spongy parenchyma being often less close, and the cuticle is thickened.

It will be observed that variations in the amount of chlorophyllous tissue appear to occur, if Herr Leist's account be compared with that of M. Bonnier. The latter, however, discovered that there would seem to be an "optimum of altitude," and that the green colour increases up to a certain limit and then decreases.

This agrees with Mr. Sorby's discovery that there is also an optimum degree of light for "greening." In speaking of the "waste and supply of colouring matters in plants," he writes :[2]—"It appears to me that their development is some

[1] *Zur Anat. einiger Keimblätter*, 8vo, Breslau, 1889. See *Bot. Centralb.*, xlii. (1890), p. 163. The above paragraph is composed from a notice in the *Journ. Royal Micr. Soc.*, 1890, p. 626. I have not seen the original.

[2] On Comparative Vegetable Chromatology. *Proc. Roy. Soc.*, No. 146, vol. xxi. 1873, p. 468.

direct function of light, until a certain quantity of each has been
formed and a sort of equilibrium established, varying in its
character according to the particular plant ; but that at the same
time the amount of each decomposed continues to increase directly
as the intensity of the light ; so that the equilibrium between
the different substances is not the same for light of different
intensities, but, after having reached a maximum, the quantity
of each more or less decreases with increased light." He then
performed an experiment with the leaves of *Aucuba Japonica*,
which is particularly sensitive to light, the leaves on the surface
of a bush being always much more spotted with yellow than
those shaded ; so that by covering half one of the former, in
three weeks' stime the two colours were sharply defined. The
result in the amounts of colouring matter was as follows.
Regarding the normal state as 100, the green of the protected
half had "Chlorophylls" increased to 150, and "Xanthophylls"
reduced to 75. Similarly for leaves of the common Holly,
those naturally shaded compared with those naturally exposed
were as follows :—Chlorophylls, 100 : 62 ; Orange Xanthophyll,
100 to 86. Mixed Xanthophylls, &c., 100 to 94. So, too, he
found that too great exposure reduced the chlorophyllian substances in lichens and seaweeds : so that it is presumably a
general fact. As a secondary result from the increase of
chlorophyllous tissue is the greater quantity of nutritive and
other materials elaborated in the plant. Thus M. Bonnier's [1]
experiments explain the presence of a relatively larger amount
of sugar, starches, essential oils, colouring matters, alkaloids,
&c., which is found in plants (living ordinarily at a lower
elevation) when they are grown in a higher Alpine situation ;
since all these products of metabolism are either directly or

[1] *Cultures Expérimentales dans les Hautes Altitudes. Comptes Rendus*, cx.
1890, p. 363 ; and *Influence des Hautes Altitudes sur les Fonctions des
Végétaux*, cxi.

indirectly dependent upon the chlorophyllous assimilation effected by plants in an Alpine climate.

The exhalation of powerful odours occurs also at high altitudes, and may perhaps perform the same use of arresting the heat as Dr. G. Volkens suggested as being the case in the deserts. Thus Sir J. D. Hooker writes :—" *Delphinium glaciale* was also abundant, exhaling a rank smell of musk. It indicates a very great elevation in Sikkim, and on my ascent far above it, therefore, I was not surprised to find water boiled at 182° 6′ (air 43°), which gives an altitude of 16,754 feet."[1]

As another instance of a plant yielding a very unexpected odour, Dr. Aitchison collected a labiate, *Teucrium serratum*, in the country traversed by the Afghan Boundary Commission, which was strongly scented with an odour exactly resembling asafœtida.[2]

DURATION.—MM. Bonnier and Flahault[3] have shown how annuals yield to perennials in point of number both in altitude and latitude. They give in their tables the proportion of annual species as 60 p.c. between 200 and 300 m. above the sea; between 600 and 1800 m. it sinks to 33 p.c.; while on altitudes above 1800 m. it is only 6 p.c. In the uppermost parts of the Alpine regions there are no annuals. Similarly Mr. Malmgren has pointed out that the plants of Spitzbergen are all perennial and have a tendency to grow in tufts.[4]

It is clear that the conditions unfavourable to the growth of annuals are low isothermic lines and short summers. Moreover,

---

[1] *Op. cit.*, p. 355 (*supra*, p. 92).
[2] A Summary of Bot. Features, &c.   *Trans. and Proc. Bot. Soc. Edin.*, 1889, p. 421 (see also *supra*, p. 84).
[3] *Ann. des Sci. Nat. Bot.*, 1878, p. 93, and 1879, p. 159; *Bull. de la Soc. Bot. de Fr.*, 1878, p. 300, and 1880, p. 103.
[4] *Journal of Botany*, America.

species which are ordinarily annuals at low levels, if growing at high elevations are found to have become perennials. Thus M. Bonnier met with *Arenaria serpyllifolia* as a perennial from 2000 to 2300 m. on. the Pyrenees. He says it there forms rhizomes some of which were three years old. *Poa annua* has subterranean ramifications of a rhizome. *Linaria alpina* is biennial above 500 m., being annual up to that height. In the more elevated regions of the Alps, where it reaches the extreme limits of vegetation, it is always perennial, and has adventitious buds which are borne upon the roots of three to five years old ; and even eight layers of wood are sometimes observable. *Senecio viscosus* is perennial both in the tap-root and base of the stem ; so also is *Ranunculus Philonotis*.

The above facts show that the prolonged duration of life of high Alpine plants is simply due to the direct action of the environment upon the plants themselves.

The development of bulbs and tubers, &c., is frequently correlated with climatic conditions which demand a perennial habit in plants if they have to survive trying periods of drought. Thus Mr. Scott Elliott[1] speaks of certain plants of the Karoo of South Africa :—Many are "bulbous or tuberous plants, and many orders have developed bulbs which usually show no trace of them; *e.g.*, the whole section *Hoarea* of *Pelargonium* is bulbous." He adds the additional important words : "One must remember that the physiognomy of a plant depends on the climate during the flowering and assimilating season only, not on that of the whole year. It is this fact which prevents one from noticing, as often as one might otherwise do, the direct influence of the climate."

PLANTS OF HIGH LATITUDES.—There is a close parallel between plants of high latitudes and those of high altitudes.

---

[1] Notes on the Regional Distribution of the Cape Flora. *Trans. Bot. Soc. Edin.*, 1891, p. 248 (see also *supra*, p. 53).

This is particularly noticeable in the following particulars: a dwarf habit, often cæspitose;[1] a perennial character, greener foliage, more brilliant flowers and fruits than at lower latitudes. There is also a greater production of substances resulting from metabolism, as honey, sugar, ethereal oils, &c.

With regard to the climatic environment, high latitudes are deficient in heat, but this is compensated for by a more prolonged sunlight during the period of growth and development; so that the increase in the quantity of chlorophyllous tissue is due to prolonged sunlight, but which is feeble in intensity.[2]

Now, although the above characteristics, as those on high altitudes, have been long known, and are readily observable in travelling, say, from the latitude of Paris northwards along the Scandinavian regions to high latitudes, the fact that they are all the outcome of the direct action of the environment has been proved by experimental cultivations, just as almost exactly similar phenomena of high altitudes have been proved to be due to similar causes. Thus, e.g., Dr. Schübeler[3] sowed seeds of different plants in different latitudes in Norway, and proved that the brilliancy of the flowers increased with the

---

[1] As examples of a tufted or cæspitose habit of growth the following plants in the Antarctic regions may be mentioned :—*Forsteria clavigera* (Stylideæ), Lord Auckland's Island ; *Drapetes muscosa* (Thymelaceæ), Hermite Island ; *Oreobalus pectinatus* (Cyperaceæ), Campbell's Island, &c. ; *Bolax glebaria* (Umbelliferæ), Falkland Islands ; *Azorella Selago* and *Lyallia Kerguelena* (Portulacaceæ), Kerguelen's Island ; *Nassauvia serpens* (Compositæ), Falkland Islands.

Many very different orders are here represented ; a similar *facies*, however, is more or less common to all.

[2] *Observations sur les Modifications des Végétaux suivant les Conditions Physiques du Milieu*, par G. Bonnier et Ch. Flahault. *Ann. des Sci. Nat. Bot.*, 6 Sér. vii. 1878, p. 93 ; also 6 Sér. ix. 1879, p. 159. See also De Candolle's *Géog. Bot.*, i. pp. 311-312.

[3] *Die Pflanzenwelt Norvegens* (Khristiania, 1875).

latitude. So great were the differences that it was difficult
to conceive that they were produced from the same batch of
seeds. The differences appeared in the first year. Similarly
seeds from Germany exhibited analogous differences. Dr.
Schübeler also made analyses of leaves of plants of the same
species grown in different parts of Norway, and found that
leaves from the northern districts were richer in chlorophyll
than those grown near Christiania.

The physical environment of high latitudes being comparable, but not quite identical, with those of high altitudes,
certain differences occur in the plant life. Thus, MM. Bonnier
and Flahault observe that in rising from the base to the
summit of the Alps, one meets successively with the sub-
Alpine zone of pines, then the Alpine flora separated from
the former by *a well-marked boundary.* On passing northwards
at the same altitude in Scandinavia, one sees *the two floras
intermixed* more and more as one reaches the highest latitudes.
It is by a very long suite of insensible transitions that one
passes from a flora almost uniquely sub-Alpine to a flora
exclusively Alpine.

Dr. Schübeler found that the enhanced greenness of the
foliage and the brilliancy of flowers are not strictly proportional
to latitude, but are *accentuated* in the higher latitudes. MM.
Bonnier and Flahault observe also, just as M. Ad. Pellat
noticed, that the same species of plants became more tomentose
in proportion as they ascended the French mountains, as,
e.g., *Ranunculus bulbosus, Oxytropis campestris, Cracca major,*
&c.; so analogous remarks can be made upon the variations
in the degree of hairiness with latitude.[1] The same frequency
of perennials in Alpine regions is exactly paralleled in high

[1] These authors give an account of very interesting investigations into
the amount of light and heat received in high latitudes, as also does M.
J. A. Broch, *Le Royaume de Norvège et le Peuple norvégien.*

latitudes; and just as annuals of low elevations *become* perennials on mountains, so do they in Arctic regions. Hence the relative number of perennials increases with both altitude and latitude. Thus of annuals there are 45 p.c. at Paris (lat. 49°); 30 p.c. at Christiania (lat. 59° 5′); 26 p.c. at Listad (lat. 61° 1′); while in Spitzbergen there are none.[1]

The significance of these statements lies in the fact mentioned above, that plants which are annuals elsewhere actually become themselves perennials when grown in these colder regions; and are, therefore, *made* to acquire the forms and habits best fitted to survive.

A feature often observed both on high altitudes and latitudes is the extreme rapidity with which the annual course of vegetation is run through during the very short summer. Thus, *e.g.*, the flowers of *Parnassia, Gnaphalium dioicum, Gentiana germanica, Solidago, Dianthus superbus,* &c., come out a month sooner in the high mountains than they do lower down, otherwise they could not ripen their seeds. Similarly, in the extreme north, the willows flower directly the sun's rays fall on them, weeks before the ground is fully thawed. How is this brought about? The answer is the same for all other adaptations. The very conditions attending a prolonged winter are the actual causes of the subsequent and necessary rapidity.

Many observers (Knight, Krasan, Frank, &c.) have found that perennial plants exposed to low temperatures during the winter rest put forth shoots more rapidly and earlier in the spring than the same plants kept warmer in the winter. It would seem that these results may depend upon at least two prominent factors, the effect of frost on the reserve food materials and the accumulation of water. As illustrating

---

[1] According to Mr. Malmgren (*Journ. of Bot.*, America).

the former, Müller-Thurgau took ten potatoes, all alike, and of about the same size and weight : he placed five in an ice-cellar, and surrounded them with ice ; the other five were kept in an ordinary house-cellar.   Those exposed to the freezing process yielded a large crop in three months after planting ; while the others, planted at the same time, and in exactly the same way, soil, &c., had as yet only begun to show shoots, and bore no tubers.   In this case the exposure to cold increased the amount of sugar in the tubers, *i.e.*, of food directly available in growth, &c. ; but whether the cold has any effect in hastening the formation of ferments, or in converting the proteids into easily assimilable substances, is not known.[1]

As an illustration of rapid growth consequent on the accumulation of water, M. W. Jännicke attributes a peculiar rapidity of growth in a *Weigela* to its growing in a shady and moist situation.   In consequence of this, the plant was retarded until May by the persistent cold of the winter, but it subsequently effected its growth with extreme rapidity.   Other plants of *Weigela* situated in dry and well-illuminated places presented no such anomaly.[2]

These cases would seem to supply us with the interpretation required.   During the prolonged period of cold on the Alps and Arctic regions, there has been a slow accumulation of water within the tissues, so that the moment the temperature rises to a sufficient height, the plant is, so to say, fully prepared to carry on the vegetative and reproductive functions at once.   Whether the frost will affect the starch in seeds

---

[1] From a notice of Herr L. Kny's work, *Sitzungsberichte der Gesellsch. Naturforsch. Freunde zu Berlin*, Nov. 15, 1887, in the *Gardener's Chronicle*, Feb. 25, 1888, p. 240.

[2] *Bildungsabweichungen an Weigelien, Berichte der deutschen botan. Gesellschaft*, Bd. ix. Heft viii. p. 266.

was not conclusively determined by Herr Kny, but he came to the conclusion that the action of frost on seeds varies in different species subjected to the same treatment, and varies with the treatment otherwise, e.g., whether the seeds are swollen or not before the frost acts.

However, the conclusion is, I think, at least justifiable hypothetically that the rapidity of the summer growth is the direct consequence of the prolonged rest and severe frost to which Alpine and Arctic plants are subjected.[1]

M. G. Bonnier has lately published a paper entitled *Les Plantes Arctiques comparées aux mêmes Espèces des Alpes et des Pyrénées,*[2] in which he shows that although, speaking generally, the Alpine floras are comparable with the Arctic, the same species being often found in both regions, yet there are certain differences which are attributable to a diversity of

---

[1] Sir J. D. Hooker, in writing about the periods when vegetation is active at different elevations on the Himalaya, says :—"The distribution of the seasons at different elevations in the Himalaya gives rise to some anomalies that have puzzled naturalists." From October to May vegetation is torpid above 14,000 feet. It is torpid above 10,000 feet from November to April, and from 6000 feet during the three months December, January, and February.

Spring begins in March, with a sudden accession of heat, above 7000 feet. "From May till August the vegetation at each elevation is (in ascending order) a month behind that below it, 4000 feet being about equal to a month of summer weather, in one sense. I mean by this, that the genera and natural orders (and sometimes the species) which flower at 8000 feet in May are not so forward at 12,000 feet till June, nor at 16,000 feet till August. After August, however, the reverse holds good ; then the vegetation is as forward at 16,000 feet as at 8000 feet. By the end of September most of the natural orders and genera have ripened their fruit in the upper zone, though they have flowered as late as July ; whereas October is the fruiting month at 12,000, and November below 10,000" (*Him. Journ.*, p. 419, note). It is possible that what is said above may explain this peculiarity in the hastening of the maturation of plants at great elevations.

[2] *Rev. Gén. de Bot.*, vi. p. 505.

external conditions, in the high altitudes and high latitudes respectively. Thus, although the total amount of serviceable light may be approximately the same, yet it is distributed very differently. Secondly, the higher one ascends above the limits of trees in mountains, the drier does the air become; but the moisture is still great in high latitudes, under certain circumstances, especially where warm and cold ocean currents touch.

M. Bonnier has shown by a careful microscopical examination of the leaves and other organs of plants from both regions that their anatomy corresponds precisely with the effects of comparative degrees of drought and moisture respectively; so that plants brought from the island Jan Mayen and Spitzbergen exhibit structures which might be called "incipiently aquatic," while those exposed to great aridity are "incipiently xerophilous."

Moreover, M. Bonnier finds that individual Alpine plants which happen to grow in moist places assume more or less the same features as those which characterise the Arctic members of the same species; and as Spitzbergen is relatively drier than Jan Mayen, precisely similar degrees of difference are found in the same species growing in these two places respectively.

The special characteristics may be summed up as follows for the Arctic individuals :—A thin cuticle, a lax and ill-defined palisadic tissue, with layers of more rounded cells. Such make the leaf thicker in a transverse section, the endoderm being a little more developed. The stems are thicker, with fewer fibro-vascular bundles than in the thinner and more woody stem of high Alpine plants. The cells of the pith and medullary rays are rounder, forming a lax tissue. From six to eight vessels occur in a fibro-vascular bundle of the Arctic plant, but from ten to twelve in that of the Alpine. In the roots, both in the Arctic and in the Alpine when growing in marshy spots, there are lacunæ with partitions of rounded cells, very similar to those in the roots of true aquatic plants.

M. Bonnier, summing up his observations, observes that these structural differences correspond with the climate; and this has been verified by experiment, for M. Lothelier has proved that in a moist atmosphere the structure of the stem and leaf at once modify themselves precisely in the same manner as is described by the author, in nature.

GENERAL CONCLUSIONS.—The conclusions arrived at from an investigation into the peculiar characteristics of plants growing in high Alpine and Arctic regions are parallel with those already deduced for sub-tropical deserts, namely, that they are the direct outcome of the action of the climate upon the responsiveness of the plants themselves. First, there are the numerous instances of plants of no affinity whatever all assuming the same features of nanism. Certain groups of shrubs and trees have leaves more and more arrested as the altitude increases; conversely some herbaceous plants have larger and greener foliage than when the same species are growing at lower altitudes and latitudes. There is not infrequently a muscoidal type, or a hirsute, villous, or tomentose condition; though many may remain glabrous. Secondly, experimental evidence has shown how many plants of the lowlands can at once acquire one or more of these features when made to grow at high altitudes and latitudes, and *vice versâ*.

Hence, as far as the vegetative organs are concerned, we arrive at the conclusion that the above-mentioned varietal sub-specific, or even it may be specific characters, are simply the result of the direct action of the environment upon the plants themselves, which by perpetuation become relatively fixed and hereditary, and all without any aid from natural selection whatever.

CHAPTER VI

ORIGIN OF THE STRUCTURAL PECULIARITIES OF MARITIME AND SALINE PLANTS

GENERAL FEATURES.—The peculiarities of maritime plants consist in some cases of a considerable degree of succulency, as of the familiar Samphire ; in others, of an extra amount of hair as compared with inland forms of the same genus or species, as *Geranium lucidum*, var. *Raii.* Again, certain species have a spiny character, as, *e.g.*, *Eryngium maritimum, Ononis spinosa*, var. *horrida.* Lastly, a glaucous hue is not uncommon, as of *Crambe maritima, Glaucium luteum*, &c.

It will be observed in these respects that there are certain peculiarities common with desert plants as well as with some Alpine and sub-Alpine species. Sir J. D. Hooker [1] noticed a certain general correspondence between the climate of some countries at the sea-level and that of the Himalaya, both in the absence of animal life and in lacking certain natural orders of plants. He thus compares New Zealand, Fuegia, and Tasmania with Scotland and Norway. He attributes the absence of life to the moist and cold atmosphere.

Perhaps it is this cause which may account for several of our maritime plants being also found on our mountains as well, or certain varieties of them. For, of course, the British mountains are not characterised by that intense aridity which pre-

---

[1] *Op. cit.*, p. 353 (*supra*, p. 92).

vails at much higher elevations in the European Alps and on other lofty ranges of mountains. The following plants will illustrate this coincidence : *Draba incana, Cochlearia officinalis*, subsp. *alpina, Silene maritima, Sagina apetala*, subsp. *maritima*, var. *alpina*. Species of *Sedum, Plantago maritima*, identical with *P. alpina* (Hoffman), *Hieracium* species, &c.

The resemblances which may be seen in plants from such widely different localities as our sea-shores, Alpine regions, and desert countries are readily explicable if the general interpretation offered in this book be accepted, viz., that certain elements of the environment are in excess ; these act upon the plants in question, and the latter respond accordingly, so that much the same results occur. Thus, if hairiness be due to a check in the development of cellular tissue, it may arise from too much heat, as in the deserts of Africa, or from too great a degree of cold, as in Alpine and Arctic regions ; both conditions causing great aridity. Succulency in the deserts, especially where the soil is saline, arises from identically the same cause as in plants on our own sea-shores.

Since the moisture of the air and soil is more charged with saline matters in maritime regions and salt marshes, it was a reasonable inference that the presence of salts was in some degree responsible for the remarkable fleshiness of such plants as *Crithmum maritimum, Salicornia herbacea*, and many others.

Experiments have justified these deductions, as well as the interpretation of the presence of a greater degree of hairiness in certain maritime plants.

As examples, the following British species and varieties of maritime plants may be mentioned, as exhibiting one or other of the above characteristics. Thus as fleshy and sub-fleshy types we have *Cochlearia, Crambe, Glaucium, Brassica oleracea, Geranium Robertianum*, var. *purpureum, Lotus corniculatus*, var.

crassifolius, Crithmum maritimum, Matricaria inodora, var. *salina,* (passing into) *M. maritima, Solanum Dulcamara,* var. *marinum.* A densely tomentose variety of this plant grows on the beach at Walmer, *Polygonum aviculare,* var. *littorale,* (passing into) *P. maritimum.*

Others might be added, but these will be sufficient to illustrate the characteristics of maritime plants which have been brought about by the direct action of their environment. This is proved by the fact that they often lose them when grown under different conditions. Thus, as has been already stated, the leaves of Samphire became flat and thin when the plant was grown in a garden; *Salsola Kali* passed gradually into *S. Tragus* as it spread up the sides of a river, and *Ononis spinosa* loses its spines in a rich soil and an abundance of moisture.

As an example of variability in glaucescence, Mr. Baker observes of the Bromeliaceous plants cultivated in the Riviera :—"As might be expected, there is a general tendency in the leaves to be more glaucous than at home."[1]

Lastly, Linnæus recorded about one hundred and fifty years ago how hairiness may disappear:—"Minui pubescentiam *Jacobæœ* vulgo dictæ *maritimæ* sæpius vidimus, id quod etiam aliis eminentibus partibus accidit."[2]

In corroboration of this statement M. Battandier observes[3] how *Buphthalmium maritimum,* which is velvety on certain maritime cliffs, becomes quite glabrous when protected from the sea. He recognises two chief maritime types: one, a succulent and glabrous; a second, velvety and more or less succulent as well. He considers that these conditions enable

---

[1] *Kew Bull. of Misc. Inf.,* January 1892, p. 10.

[2] *Philos. Bot.,* § 272.

[3] *Quelques Mots sur les Causes de la Localisation des Espèces d'une Région. Bull. de la Soc. Bot. de Fr.,* 1806, p. 189.

plants to resist the deleterious action of the sea. Hence he noticed how certain inland plants, elsewhere thick or velvety, as *Cotyledon umbilicus* and *Artemisia arborescens*, do not suffer by the sea. He also thinks that "it is probable that it is under the irritating influence of the water of the sea that these modifications have been produced." As other examples I have noticed that primroses and some plants of *Laurustinus*, &c., are almost woolly at Cannes, though they are far from being so in England.

ANATOMY OF SUCCULENT TISSUES.—With regard to the anatomy of the succulent tissues of maritime plants, Herr Brick [1] finds that there is a strongly developed cortical parenchyma, with an invariable presence of a vascular bundle-sheath, with a rarity of starch in the chlorophyll grains. M. Lesage has lately shown that salts cause a decrease in the formation of starch. Herr Brick recognises three types : (1) a cortical parenchyma composed of round cells with triangular intercellular spaces, the chlorophyll being either distributed through the parenchyma or limited to a special outer zone of the cortex (*Honckenya peploides* and *Cakile maritima*); (2) cortical parenchyma consisting of round cells with large and nearly regular air-passages (*Aster Tripolium, Glaux maritima*) ; (3) cortical parenchyma, that of an ordinary leaf, the chlorophyll being in palisade cells (*Salsola Kali, Salicornia herbacea*).

M. Lesage,[2] in comparing the anatomy of species of plants growing by the sea and inland, finds that in more than half the cells of the epidermis show no appreciable difference.

---

[1] *Schrift-Naturf. Gesell.* Danzig, vii. 1888, 108. See also *Natur-forscher*, xxi. 1888, p. 214.

[2] *Recherches Expérimentales sur les Modifications des Feuilles chez les Plantes Maritimes. Rev. Gén. de Bot.*, tom. ii. p. 54, Pl. 7, 8, 9.

In four species there were more decided differences, as shown by the following ratios, (1) in the size of the epidermal cells, and (2) in the thickness of the leaves. V.M. represents the maritime variety, and V.T. the inland terrestrial one.

	I.		2.	
	V.M.	V.T.	V.M.	V.T.
Cakile maritima	2	: 1	4–5	: 1
Beta vulgaris .	3–4	: 1	8	: 3
Silene maritima	4–5	: 1	4	: 1
Aster Tripolium	1·5	: 1	3	: 1

In *Silene maritima* and *Cakile maritima*, there was an increase in the proportion of about two to one in thickness of the epidermal wall in the maritime plants. In others it was less than twice as thick, and more generally there was no difference.

With regard to the palisade tissue, the general thicknes may result from a development in volume of all the cells, or by a formation of a greater number of layers. These variations can affect all or a part of the mesophyll, as well as, but especially, the palisade. Thus of fifty-four species which showed a thickness in the leaf of the maritime variety, eleven exhibited an equal development of all the elements; seven species showed an extra development of the palisade cells in volume and length, without increasing the number of layers; while five species showed an increase in the number of palisadic layers. Lastly, thirty-one species presented an increase of volume and of length of the palisade cells, at the same time that the palisadic layers increased in number.

With regard to intercellular spaces, M. Lesage observes that if the palisadic tissue is more developed, the mesophyll will have its lacunæ reduced in size, since the palisade cells are arranged in such a way as not to suppress completely the

I

intercellular spaces, but to reduce them considerably. Generally speaking, the maritime leaf is less lacunous than the inland type.

The median ribs of the thicker leaves of maritime plants are also rather larger than those of inland plants, but not in the same proportion as the thickness of the leaf itself. Thus in *Crithmum maritimum* the proportion is 225 to 125 for the thickness of the leaf; that of the mid-ribs is 65–60 to 35–30. In *Silene maritima,* however, while the thickness of the leaves is as 168 to 60, that of the fibro-vascular cords is as 23–30 to 16–16.

There is no appreciable difference in the size of the vessels themselves.

With regard to chlorophyll, in some cases M. Lesage was unable to see if there was any difference; in others it was very marked. Thus *Thesium humifusum* and *Cakile maritima* showed a great difference in this respect, the grains being much smaller in the maritime plants. In some species the grains of chlorophyll, though of an equal diameter, are less abundant in the corresponding layers of mesophyll, as is the case with *Atriplex portulacoides*.

In other cases, the grains, more or less unequal in size, are less numerous in cells of the same layer, as one can see in the leaves of *Trifolium arvense*.

The four conclusions to which M. Lesage arrives are as follows :—

1. Maritime plants have mostly thicker leaves, but all plants do not follow this rule in a pronounced manner.

2. The thickness of the leaf is accompanied by a great development of palisadic tissue.

3. The lacunæ and intercellular spaces tend to be reduced in the leaves of maritime plants.

4. Chlorophyll is generally less abundant in maritime plants,

either by a reduction in volume or by a reduction of the number of grains.

EXPERIMENTAL EVIDENCE.—M. Lesage [1] carried out a large series of experiments with a great variety of plants, in order to see if watering them with salt dissolved in the water would produce results similar to the normally fleshy structure so characteristic of many maritime plants. Such proved to be the case. Thus with *Pisum sativum* he found that the thickness of the leaf became greater, and the palisade tissue increased in thickness, while intercellular spaces and the chlorophyll diminished. *Lepidium sativum* gave more marked results. The mesophyll presented six layers in the four cases forming the subjects of his experiments. The palisade tissue was more developed in a radial direction and possessed an extra layer. The lacunæ were less pronounced, and the chlorophyll was less abundant. The epidermis and the vascular cords do not follow the same variations in thickness. On the average, if the leaf is much thicker, then the epidermis and the nerves are only a trifle thicker than ordinarily.

M. Lesage [2] sums up his results, showing that his experiments completely verify the deduction that the succulency of maritime, and we may add saline, plants is the direct result of the presence of salts in the water imbibed by them. M. Lesage does not say how he thinks the turgidity is actually brought about; but Herr C. Brick suggests that it may be due to the formation of salts of an organic acid with the soda with which they are so abundantly supplied.

I give the above. histological peculiarities somewhat in detail, in order to show how a maritime environment acts on the minutest elements of the tissues of plants, until they

[1] *Op. cit.*, p. 110 (*supra*, p. 128).

[2] *Op. cit.*, p. 172-173. M. Lesage has also elsewhere contributed papers on this subject, *e.g.*, to *Comptes Rendus*, cix. 1889, p. 204, and cxii. p. 892.

become more or less fixed and characteristic, at least as long as they continue to grow under the same conditions. They thus furnish morphological characters which botanists regard as classificatory.

M. Costantin arrived at similar conclusions, for he says:—
" The development of plants growing in saline districts exhibits different degrees of thickness of the foliage, of the stems, and of the fruits, a change in the green tint of the plant, and in some cases an abundant production of hairs upon the whole plant." [1]

M. Costantin [2] also refers to *Artemisia campestris* as a plant, the maritime form of which, viz., var. *maritima*, has leaves which are very thick. He also mentions that *Hieracium eriophorum*, when cultivated in the Botanic Garden at Bordeaux, lost the hair which it possesses when growing in maritime sands.

In corroboration of the facts given above, I will here add a communication received from M. J. Lloyd of Nantes, who thus writes:—" I will repeat what I said in three editions of *Flore de l'Ouest* about our inland plants growing near the sea. 'Trompé par ce changement de port, le botaniste de l'intérieur est généralement tenté de voir dans ces végétaux rabougris et velus, à feuilles charnues et quelquefois salées, des espèces ou des variétés nouvelles. Plusieurs de ces formes ont été distinguées sous le nom de var. *maritima, nana, uniflora, carnosa, succulenta, salina;* mais toutes les plantes de l'intérieur pourraient avec autant de droit avoir leur variété "maritime," car toutes se modifient en approchant de la mer.' "

Mr. Lloyd also supplies me with the following examples:—

---

[1] *La Flore du Littoral. Journ. de Bot.*, 1887, No. 3, p. 45.

[2] *Recherches sur la Structure de la Tige des Plantes Aquatiques. Ann. des Sci. Nat.*, 6 Sér. xix. 1884, p. 287, note.

"*Linosyris* at Belle Isle is dwarf, two inches high, but by culture it grows taller every year. *Cochlearia officinalis* on rocks and pebbles has thick leaves, less so on muddy banks of rivers. *Hieracium eriophorum* far from the sea is no longer *densissime lanatum*. *Helianthemum guttatum*, var. *maritimum*, gradually returns to the inland form in receding from the seashore. *Hieracium umbellatum* is dwarf and thick on sea-rocks. *Pteris aquilina* on damp rocks is so different from the common form, that no one at first would think it belongs to the same species."

M. Gadeceau, who is familiar with the flora of Western France, also writes me as follows:—"The position of Nantes, in which I live, enables me to verify the fact of the influence which the neighbourhood of the sea exercises on inland plants. In fact, they all undergo more or less modification as they approach the coast, and nearly all our species ought to have a var. *maritima*.

"On the very confines of our coasts *Ulex europœus* forms stunted bushes; on the long points which stretch far into the sea, these bushes are scarcely some decimetres high. Similarly, a great number of plants from inland have become dwarf or creeping (procumbent), *e.g.*, the following list, which has been verified by myself:—*Silene Otites*, var. *umbellata*, Ll. ; *Geranium columbinum ; Althœa hirsuta ; Linum angustifolium ; Medicago striata ; Ononis repens*, var. B. (Ll., *Fl. d'Ouest*); *Ornithopus perpusillus ; Sarothamnus scoparius ; Trifolium angustifolium, T. striatum* (reverts to the type on being sown); *Asperula cynanchica ; Artemisia campestris*, var. *maritima*, Ll. ; *Gnaphalium luteo-album ; Hieracium umbellatum ; Linosyris vulgaris ; Senecio vulgaris* (few-flowered and rayed on maritime sands); *Calluna vulgaris ; Erythrœa Centaurium*, var. *capitata*, Ll. (non *E. cap.*, Towns.); *Trixago Apula ; Plantago maritima ; Atriplex angustifolia*, var. B. *angus-*

tissima, Ll. ; *Asparagus officinalis*, var. *B. maritimus*, Dun. (this variety reproduces itself notwithstanding being long cultivated in the interior) ; *Juncus capitatus ; Anthoxanthum odoratum* (*A. Lloydii*, Jord.) ; *Dactylis glomerata ; Holcus lanatus.*

"*Secondly*, There are inland species which have become more downy or hairy, or even woolly, as, *e.g.*, *Helianthemum guttatum*, var. *maritimum*, Ll. ; *Herniaria glabra*, var. *B. ciliata*, Ll. ; (*H. ciliata*, Bab.) ; *Trifolium arvense*, var. *perpusillum*, D.C. ; *Thrincia hirta ; Jasione montana*, var. *maritima*, Ll. ; *Achillea millefolium*, var. *candicans*, Le Gall. ; *Mentha rotundifolia*, var. *maritima*, Nob. ; *Stachys recta*, var. *lanata*, Nob. ; *Plantago Coronopus*, var. *lanuginosa*, Nob. (Belle Isle) ; *P. lanceolata*, var. *lanuginosa*, Ll. ; *Kœleria cristata*, Pers., var. *villosa*, Ll., &c., &c.

"*Thirdly*, On the banks of salt marshes certain inland plants put on fleshy leaves. These are chiefly *Chrysanthemum inodorum*, var. *maritimum*, Lloyd, and *Atriplex latifolia*, var. *salina*, Lloyd. The Chrysanthemum grows in the sand on maritime rocks, and differs besides from the type in that the ribs of the achenes are oblong, not rounded, and the intervals reduced to simple lines. When sown this form reverts the first year to the inland type.[1]

"*Fourthly*, *Hypochœris glabra* forms in the sand and in seaside meadows pediculated tufts. This character disappears the first year after sowing inland.[1]

"*Lastly*, In the alluvial lands recently formed by the excavation of our maritime canal of the Lower Loire I have been able to observe how the mud, rich in detritus, has stimulated vegetation, and my observations have been embodied in a pamphlet."

CONCLUSION.—The general result of these observations on

[1] *Flore de l'Ouest*, Lloyd, 4th edit., p. 192.

the structure of maritime and saline plants is thus seen to be distinctly parallel with those on Desert, Alpine, and Arctic plants, &c., in that while on the one hand similar characteristics are noticeable in numerous plants of no affinity whatever, but simply living under the same environment, experimental evidence invariably shows how these features can be either more or less produced by simulating the normal conditions of growth, or can be restrained, by growing maritime plants in soils and climates of very different characters from those which obtain by the sea. In other words, the peculiarities of maritime and saline plants are in all cases actually caused by their environment. These then become characters recognised by systematic botanists, as varietal, specific, or otherwise.

CHAPTER VII

ORIGIN OF THE STRUCTURAL PECULIARITIES OF PHANEROGAMOUS AQUATIC PLANTS

(*Histology of Roots*)

PRELIMINARY OBSERVATIONS. — There is probably nothing which acts more quickly in the production of a change of structure in plants than an aquatic medium, and by which the responsiveness of protoplasm is more readily incited. Experimental evidence is so easily obtained, and the results are so convincing, that if one might argue from analogy derived from this environment alone, it would seem to be almost enough to establish the evidence of the influences of the external conditions being the true and sufficient origin of variations in plants.

Well-marked characteristic features due to an aquatic habitat are seen in roots, stems, and foliage, and in some cases even in flowers as well. Allowing for various modifications, one recognises them in plants from all parts of the vegetable kingdom, which include flowering plants and vascular cryptogams as well as aquatic thallophytes.

The peculiarities referred to are best observed by contrasting them with the corresponding structures in the aërial and subterranean parts of terrestrial plants, and especially of those which are allied to the aquatic species, and by comparing the land forms with the water forms of one and

the same amphibious species. It will be then at once per-
ceived that the great feature which stands out pre-eminently
observable as an invariable effect of a watery medium is
degeneracy. Not only is this obviously apparent in the forms
of organs, but in the most pronounced manner even in the
minutest details of histology. Thus, *e.g.*, M. Chatin observes,
after a prolonged study of the anatomy of aquatic plants :[1]—

"Les genres *Vallisneria, Anacharis, Hydrilla et Udora,*
tous submergés et dépourvus de tout élément vasculaire,
justifient mes aperçus, et disent assez que la dégradation
organique est, dans le règne végétal, aussi bien que dans le
règne animal, en rapport avec le milieu habité par les
espèces."

Since aquatic plants live and thrive in water as their
normal medium, the inference is obvious that this degeneracy
of structure, as compared with that of land plants, so far
from involving any disadvantage to the former, really puts
them into perfect equilibrium or harmony with their environment ; in fact, the adjective "adaptive" may be applied to
the word "degeneration." Consequently those structures
which are essential to an aërial existence—as, *e.g.*, lignified
supportive tissues—being no longer wanted, disappear, as
the stems are not subject to the strain (due to gravity) which
induces their formation on land ; while new features—such
as the aëriferous canals—are developed instead.

Degeneracy, therefore, in plant life, does not necessarily
imply anything injurious, but simply represents features of
an arrested, or at least simpler character, which are in perfect
correlation with the requirements or adaptations to an aquatic
or other existence.

The literature upon the structure of the various organs of

---

[1] *Anatomie comparée des Végétaux,* vol. i. p. 30.

aquatic plants is very extensive; and the difficulty lies in stating (rather from an *embarras de richesse* than any paucity of observations), as briefly as is compatible with the object in view, their main features.

I may add that I have myself experimented with several terrestrial plants by growing them in water, as well as studied amphibious plants, growing naturally both in water and on land, so\that to a considerable extent I can corroborate the results obtained by other observers.

As with previous cases, the argument that aquatic plants have acquired their peculiarities through the direct action of the medium in which they grow is based on the same two-fold grounds : first, that of comparative anatomy, derived from innumerable coincidences and correlations in aquatic plants from all parts of the vegetable kingdom and all parts of the world.; and secondly, from experimental verification. Taken together, the evidence is more than abundant to establish the truth of the proposition.

THE ROOT-PRODUCING EFFECT OF WATER.—Commencing with a study of roots, the first point to note, with regard to the influences of water upon the production and alteration of the structure of roots, is that nearly all parts of plants, if placed suitably in contact with moisture, can develop roots. Of course gardeners are familiar with this fact, and are thereby enabled to propagate by layering, cuttings, and fragments of leaves, bulb-scales, &c. In these cases the plants may have no natural tendency to produce such adventitious roots before the stimulating presence of moisture encourages them to respond to it and to develop them.

In many cases, however, it is the regular habit of the plant to produce roots at the nodes or elsewhere, like the strawberry, and they will commence to protrude them even without the presence of moisture, as when a strawberry-runner is tied up to a stick and made to grow vertically. In this case, not only is the runner checked in its growth, but the roots soon cease to elongate. This experiment proves that the *habit* or *predisposition* to produce roots from runners is hereditary or a constitutional character. Of course strawberry runners normally grow in contact with the soil, and therefore readily strike root at every node; but many plants, such as the blackberry, some ferns, &c., send their shoots or elongated fronds, respectively, first into the air, and they only reach the ground after it may be a long period of growth; but as soon as the terminal point touches the ground, it strikes root. Here again there is a predisposition which is called into action as soon as the fitting external condition, namely, a moist soil, is obtained.

As examples may be mentioned *Rubus fruticosus*, vars. *rhamnifolius* and *corylifolius*, which form a "callus" at the terminal bud of the barren shoots, from which roots arise; on the other hand, var. *suberectus* does not do so. *Solanum Dulcamara* often roots in a similar manner. *Adiantum caudatum, Asplenium rhizophyllum*, and *Scolopendrium sibiricum* have long tapering points at the ends of the fronds, of several inches in length, capable of developing a bud at the apex; while *Adiantum lunulatum* continually roots like a runner. These all strike root when in contact with the soil. It is difficult not to believe that both the callus in the blackberry, and the tapering points with their buds in the case of the ferns, have been a direct result of the stimulus of moisture.

M. H. Devaux[1] has proved that the lenticels of potatoes take on an extraordinary development when they are placed in moist air, or better still, when they are completely sub-

---

[1] *Hypertrophie des Lenticelles chez la Pomme de Terre et chez quelques autres Plantes. Bull. de la Soc. Bot. de Fr.*, Sér. 2, tom. xiii. p. 48, 1890.

merged. He has observed analogous facts on the stems of the poplar, and upon the tigellum of the poplar germinating in water, &c. The phenomenon is facilitated by heat, and appears to be better produced in light. The author regards this hypertrophy of lenticels as representing an adaptation of the plant to the exterior condition of great humidity.

Herr Klebahn [1] has also proved that in *Solanum Dulcamara* and *Herminiera Elaphroxylon* one finds in the bark below each lenticel the germ of a root; the adventitious roots always proceed from the development of these root-germs, and it is sufficient to put a fragment of a stem into water in order to soon see the roots developing through the lenticels.

Hence, from these few examples, which are sufficient to illustrate the general principle, we may recognise two conditions: first, a general property or power of rooting at any point, though it may be more especially at the nodes, when moisture is applied to the place; secondly, a constitutional and hereditary predisposition to form roots at these and other points, &c., in a certain but very large number of plants, from all parts of the vegetable kingdom.

My contention is, therefore, that the latter plants have acquired this predisposition or hereditary character from the constant habit of producing roots in contact with the ground or water, so that what is a general property of plant life becomes a specialised feature in such plants.

Besides causing the production of adventitious roots on stems and other parts of plants, moisture may bring about a great increase of secondary and subsequent rootlets from a main or taproot. If, for example, a root of *Rubus*, Alder, or other plant, reach a river or ditch or field-drain, it will sometimes produce an enormous and dense mass of root-fibres.

---

[1] *Ueber Wurzelanlagen unter Lenticellen bei Herminiera Elaphroxylon und Solanum Dulcamara.* Flora, 1891, p. 125, Taf. iv.

It is not infrequently that drain-pipes get completely choked up by them. As another instance of remarkable growth, I would remind the reader of the turnip root, the apex of which penetrated a drain-pipe. The presence of water stimulated the growth, but instead of swelling, it simply grew at the apex till it was more than six feet in length, and only one third of an inch in diameter at the summit.[1]

This power of elongating may perhaps account for the peculiarly elongated tips to the fronds of the ferns mentioned above. .

THE EFFECTS OF WATER UPON THE TISSUES OF ROOTS.—Roots may be subterranean, aquatic, or aërial; and comparative anatomy shows that there are considerable differences in their histological structures, according as they belong to either one of the three kinds.

A typical subterranean root has the following elements near its apex. The epidermis is usually of so simple a character, that some botanists prefer to call it an "epithelium," and it may or may not have some of its cells prolonged into root-hairs. Then follows a variable amount of cortical cellular tissue, until the innermost layer of the cortex or endoderm is reached. Some one or more layers of the cortex may have strengthening bands or be sclerotised in various ways. The cells of the endoderm form a more or less complete cylinder, and have, as a rule, the radial walls of the cells characterised by a dark spot in the middle, as seen in a transverse section. It is apparently due to a fold in the membrane, or is perhaps suberised. Beneath the endoderm is the layer or layers of active parenchymatous cells constituting the pericycle, sometimes called the radiciferous tissue, as it is the source of secondary roots. The xylem and phloëm bundles alternate

---

[1] Referred to on p. 53, *supra*.

in position with the rudimentary cambium adjacent to and within the latter. These two elements are embedded in ground-tissue, which completes the structure, of the central cylinder. Besides the cambium and the pericycle, certain layers of cortex may retain a merismatic character, and give rise to additional features, such as cortical fibres or suberous tissue, &c. Lastly, the apex possesses a root-cap.

Now, every one of the above-mentioned elements can undergo a change of some sort or another, according to the requirements of the plant or to alterations in the environment; for experiments prove that one and the same root begins *at once* to respond to the new external conditions, as soon as it is made to grow in an altered medium, whether it be air, earth, or water.

Moreover, it is important to observe that the alterations of the tissues which thus ensue upon an enforced change of environment are identically the same as those features which normally characterise roots growing in a medium of the same kind. This experimental investigation at once verifies the deduction that all such differences as regularly occur between terrestrial and aquatic plants (for peculiarities are not limited to roots) have been the actual results of their habitats.

THE EPIDERMIS OF ROOTS.—The chief variable feature of the epidermis of roots is the production or absence of root-hairs. Differences in their presence or absence are often characteristic of varieties and species. Thus, if their roots be wholly and deeply immersed in water, plants are usually destitute of them, as, *e.g.*, *Callitriche*, *Nymphœa*, *Nasturtium*, &c. On the other hand, I have found that the long dependent roots of plants of *Hydrocharis*, which float on the surface, are densely clothed with them, such being apparently a consequence, in that case, of some degree of light. Dr. M.

T. Masters[1] has noted that "plants with the thick fleshy and woody roots rarely produce them; as of the Crocus, Tulip, Hyacinth, *Sonchus arvensis*, *Taraxicum*, and many others;" so that root-hairs are poorly developed or are absent altogether in some plants and occur abundantly on others. In these cases they might, therefore, be taken as a diagnostic character.

M. Chatin[2] observed that root-hairs were formed when roots came in contact with any obstacle, which he considered as sufficient to account for their formation. M. Mer,[3] too, also attributed the production of root-hairs to an arrest of growth caused by some obstacle. He finds that radical hairs are much longer and more abundant as the growth of the root is slowed. Dr. Masters found that when mustard was sown in rammed clay, "the radicle penetrated it to reach the sides of the pot. Having done so, the roots produced an abundance of root-hairs." This he attributes to the presence of a thin film of moisture, and not solely to the obstruction. As a rule, they are certainly more abundant in a loose porous soil, *cæteris paribus*, than in a heavy one.

M. Costantin observed that roots bearing hairs which are few and short in water have them much longer if the roots be in earth, and acquire the greatest development in moist air.

The general result of these and other experiments shows that the presence, in a greater or less degree, or the absence of root-hairs varies according to circumstances, and that when different species grow normally under correspondingly various

[1] *Journ. Roy. Hort. Soc.*, vol. v. p. 174.
[2] *Anatomie des Plantes aériennes de l'Ordre des Orchidées. Mem. de la Soc. Imp. des Sci. de Cherbourg*, tom. iv. p. 11, 1856.
[3] *De la Constitution des Poils Radicaux. Ass. Franc. pour l'Av. des Sci.*, 1880, p. 688.

conditions, they are provided or not, as the case may be; the natural inference is that the environment has produced the results which are now constitutional, hereditary, and characteristic of such species or genera respectively.

THE CORTEX OF ROOTS.—The next element to be considered below the epidermis is the cortex of the roots of aquatic plants. With regard to this, as also the medulla when present, while in some cases there is only a more or less irregular separation of the cells, as in *Althenia*,[1] the intercellular spaces may increase in complexity until a very perfect and symmetrically arranged system of aëriferous canals is formed, with or without the presence of horizontal cellular diaphragms.

This system of lacunæ is one of the most marked and constant features of the roots and stems, and, we may add, the petioles and blades of aquatic plants generally, of whatever natural orders to which they may belong. Hence it is obviously an adaptive character, and is quite independent of any affinities.

The cellular tissue is generally throughout more delicate than that of the cortex of terrestrial plants, the walls of the cells being thinner and devoid of the extra thickening materials which produce elsewhere sclerotised, lignified, or suberised elements.

No special change appears in the endoderm beyond the general arrest of all thickening processes, which are often observed in that of rhizomes, &c.

THE CENTRAL CYLINDER OF ROOTS. — With regard to the central cylinder, very obvious degrees of degeneracy may be seen in the elements of the xylem especially, the vascular system of the central cylinder being always much reduced. The actual number of vessels of all sorts is less than in land

---

[1] *Recherches sur la Végétation et la Structure de l'Althenia filiformis, Petit.* Par M. Ed. Prillieux. *Ann. des Sci. Nat.*, 5 Sér. ii. 1864, p. 169, Pl. 16, fig. 1.

plants, and not infrequently they are wanting altogether ; for as they decrease in number, so do they in construction, passing from spirals or true tracheæ to barred (Fr. *rayées*), thence to " liber-cells " without thickenings, and finally to total absorption, a lacuna occupying the place.

M. Ph. van Tieghem [1] has described and illustrated four types showing successive degrees of degradation. In the first group the ordinary organisation is maintained, but with a diminution of the number of vessels of the wood or of the phloëm elements. In *Hydrocharis Humboldtii* each vascular bundle possesses no more than one vessel, each phloëm bundle is constituted by a single thread of narrow or elongated cells.

Of the second type *Elodea canadensis* affords a good example. In this the cells obviously destined to become vessels absorb their walls, in general, before their thickness has become appreciable.

Thirdly, in *Naias major* there still exists in the central cylinder two layers of simple cells around a central cavity. The external layer is the pericycle, the interior *ought* to be differentiated into xylem and phloëm, but the transformation does not take place.

Fourthly and lastly, in the *Lemnaceæ* the arrest is still greater, for the central cylinder is no longer formed. There is only a single layer of cells surrounding an axial lacuna. The mother-cells of the xylem and phloëm systems are not even differentiated before absorption takes place.

M. Chatin adds many other cases, and the reader will find ample illustrations of these facts in the plates given in his well-known work. There are also details to which M. van Tieghem does not refer. Thus, gradual degenerations in the thickening of vessels is seen from true spiral vessels to cavities replacing

---

[1] *Symétrie de Structure des Plantes. Ann. des Sci. Nat.,* 5 Sér. tom. xiii. p. 159. See also Chatin's *Anatomie comparée des Végétaux,* tom. i.

them ; as, for example, in *Ottelia alismoides* the xylem bundles of the root has true spirals or tracheæ. In *Hydrocharis* there are none, but "barred"[1] vessels replace them. The stolon, however, has true spirals. Generally it may be observed that the roots of aquatic plants undergo a greater degree of arrest than the stems of the same plants.

In *Stratiotes aloides* the root has no vessels, but what Chatin calls "fibres-cellules," elongated tubes with obliquely truncated ends, and which seem to be formed of cells which *ought* to have become differentiated into vessels. The degradation undergone by vessels seems to be from "spirals" to "bars," then "punctations," thence to an absence of any thickening. The vessels subsequently become replaced by "fibrous cells." Lastly, a total absorption takes place, when a long and narrow lacuna occupies its position.

Of these varieties punctated and barred vessels appear to be the most prevalent in aquatic roots.[2]

Mirbel[3] observed that punctations, bars, and spirals may occur on one and the same vessel, and called them "mixed tubes," and that it can assume successively these different appearances. Thus he says : "A trachea of a stem can terminate in the root in a moniliform vessel, become a false trachea in the node at the base of the branch, run through the latter under the form of a punctated tube, and take, in the leaves or petals, the form of trachea."[4]

---

[1] I adopt this term as perhaps better expressing their appearance than "*rayées.*" It is a sort of imperfect scalariform, or perhaps the scalariform tissue of Ferns may be regarded as a well-pronounced differentiated state of barred vessels.

[2] They occur in parasitic plants, from an analogous, though, of course, a different cause of degeneracy.

[3] *Elém. de Phys. Vég.*, Pl. x. fig. 14. See also Turpin, *Icon.*, Pl. i. fig. 11.

[4] Some authors denied Mirbel's assertion, but it is in general accordance with my own experience of the ease with which spirals can become

In aquatics the punctated vessels may closely simulate punctated fibres, the chief differences being in the lessened diameter of the latter and the more or less oblique position of the septa. Then these pass into thin-walled fibres of the same shape, and finally become "fibrous cells," when they may contain starch.

The general conclusion that one appears to arrive at is, that in the course of the differentiation of vessels, horizontal elliptical spaces are at first left, giving rise to the appearance of bars; this is the first form. If these be very regular, they acquire the scalariform character so familiar to us in Cryptogams, which thus retain permanently an elementary type. Annular vessels would seem to come next, or perhaps tracheæ, or true spiral vessels might be considered as contemporaneous with them. Reticulated and pitted vessels, as of oak-wood, I take to be further differentiations by an increased lignification. It may be added that reticulated as well as spiral vessels may have the more elementary character of bars on the same surface. This may be seen in Chatin's figure of *Boschniakia glabra*[1] and in *Obolaria virginiana*.[2]

Degradation by water appears, then, simply to reverse this order; thus in *Trapa natans* the vessels are all ringed, very rarely with a tendency to the spiral for part of their length. M. Barnéoud thus describes them:—" Ils se brisent au contraire à une faible traction en grands anneaux distincts qui flottent au milieu des gouttes d'eau dans lesquelles on les observe. Il n'y a aucune trace de véritables trachées parfaitement déroulables, et telles qu'on les remarque dans la plupart des

degraded. Of course, one knows that annular and reticulated vessels are allied to spirals, as the spiral band can become reticulated or break up into rings in the same vessel. But these latter are *variations*, and not necessarily *degradations*.

[1] *Op. cit.*, vol. i. Pl. xxiv.   [2] Vol. i. Pl. xxviii.

plantes phanérogames. Ce fait s'accorde ici très bien avec l'opinion de la plupart des anatomistes, qui considèrent les organes de la végétation, et en particulier les tiges et les racines des plantes aquatiques, comme généralement dépourvues de vraies trachées."[1]

With regard to the mechanical supportive system, M. Costantin remarks that an aquatic medium determines the reduction of it. This I can corroborate, for it is shown, for example, in the root and stem of *Bidens cernua* when the plant grows in water, and not on dry ground. There is in individuals growing in the former situation a total absence of sclerenchyma on the outside of the fibro-vascular cords, and no woody fibre; whereas both elements are well-developed in the terrestrial plants.

The Root-Cap or Pileorhiza.—I have described elsewhere the marked differences between the root-cap of Endogens and that which prevails in Exogens, and shown that the former type is found in aquatic Exogens, as the *Nymphœaceæ*, and some parasites. The differences being associated with other characters of the root, they all conjointly conspire to prove that their peculiarities are attributable to the direct action of the medium in which the roots habitually grow.[2]

The general effects of an aquatic medium upon roots may be summed up as follows:—It increases the volume of the cortical lacunæ. It diminishes the medulla and reduces the fibrous and vascular systems. Like aquatic stems, roots developed in water recall by their structure that of subterranean organs, but are different by the presence of lacunæ and by a less development of the vascular elements. Lastly,

---

[1] *Anatomie et Organogénie du Trapa natans. Ann. des Sci. Nat.*, Sér. 3. 1848, p. 229, Pl. xiii. figs. 12–16.

[2] A Theoretical Origin of Endogens from Exogens *Journ. Linn. Soc. Bot.*, xxix. p. 507.

lignine is formed with difficulty in water, as it also is in obscurity and underground.

The mass of observations on the anatomy of aquatic plants made by numerous botanists collectively, point by their uniformity to the conclusion that all these various degenerations are the actual effects produced by the action of the water upon the roots, which thus become arrested in responding to the external influences. These results are now permanent features, and are characteristic of species, genera, and orders, and even to the whole class of Endogens. With regard to the numerous points of structure proving an aquatic origin of Endogens, there is a very marked one in roots which may be here mentioned. It is a well-recognised feature of Endogens that on germinating the axial or primary root is either not developed (as in wheat) or is very transient (maize and palms), while adventitious roots are developed instead in ascending series from the stem. A precisely similar procedure is seen in germinating aquatic plants of Exogens, as in Water-lilies, *Trapa*, &c.

The cause of this arrest, which is now hereditary and characteristic of terrestrial Endogens as well as aquatic ones, appears to be, that as the development of the primary root depends upon the assimilative powers of the first leaves formed, and as these are more or less arrested in water-plants, the axial root is accordingly arrested also.[1]

[1] For further details the reader is referred to "The Origin of Endogens," &c. *Journ. Linn. Soc. Bot.*, xxix. p. 505.

CHAPTER VIII

PHANEROGAMOUS AQUATIC PLANTS—*(continued)*

(Histology of Stems and Leaves)

SUBMERGED CONTRASTED WITH AËRIAL STEMS.—In order to perceive how water brings about modifications in the histological elements of stems, it will be advisable first to contrast the tissues of aquatic with those of aërial stems ; as, *e.g.*, of corresponding parts in amphibious plants, and also different parts of one and the same stem which grows out of the water into the air, Secondly, they can be compared with those of subterranean stems, either when these latter are also submerged or beneath a dry soil.

After having shown, as briefly as is advisable, the differences which occur naturally, it will be seen that precisely the same results follow from experiments.

M. Costantin [1] has published very careful comparisons between the anatomical structures of aquatic, aërial, and subterranean stems, of which I propose to give a brief epitome and to add further matters.

He illustrates differences in the epidermis, cortex, lacunæ, collenchyma, endoderm and central cylinder, including the fibro-vascular cords.

---

[1] *Ann. des Sci. Nat. Bot.*, 6 Sér. tom. xix. 1884, p. 287. See also his paper *Etudes sur les Feuilles des Plantes aquatiques. Ann. des Sci. Nat.*, 7 Sér. tom. iii. p. 94.

He observes that just as the increase of the lacunæ will be shown to be the first result established by experiment, when stems normally aërial are kept submerged, so a less proportion is always apparent when one compares the aërial stem of an amphibious plant with that of the aquatic form, or the aërial to the aquatic part of one and the same stem. Thus, for example, he describes *Mentha aquatica*, a branch of a terrestrial plant being kept below the surface of the water :—" In this new medium the stem enlarges, its angles are less pronounced, and its surface is glabrous. The internal changes are equally well marked : the lacunæ of the aquatic part, which is the youngest, are considerable ; the cortex has consequently assumed an important increase in volume. It may be observed that while the lacunæ of the cortex are *schizogeneous*[1] and enlarged in water, the central medullary one is *lysigenous*.[2] This latter diminishes or is absent from the reduced size of the diameter of the central cylinder, through degeneracy caused by the plant growing in water."

The above differences are equally true for Exogens, Endogens, and vascular Cryptogams, as *Equisetum*.

With regard to collenchyma, it is reduced in amount or absent in aquatic stems. In the case of the *Mentha aquatica*, the terminal shoot held under water gradually curved upwards,

---

[1] That is, caused by the *separation* of the cells.

[2] That is, caused by the *laceration* of the cells. On the other hand, M. Barnéoud describes the formation of lacunæ in the cortex of *Trapa natans* as being lysigenous, and observes that there is much analogy between them and those of *Hippuris vulgaris*, *Myriophyllum*, some species of *Potamogeton*, and *Callitriche verna* (*Sur l'Anatomie et l'Organogénie du Trapa natans*, Ann. des Sci. Nat., Sér. 3, 1848, p. 228, Pl. 13, figs. 12–16).

The origin of lacunæ I would hypothetically attribute to the accumulation of air in the tissues, as it cannot escape, there being no stomata. Irregular lysigenous cavities are first formed ; but subsequently symmetrical tubes, &c., are produced ; a feature which has become hereditary in aquatic plants.

To sustain the erect position supportive tissues were required, so that collenchyma was immediately developed to meet the strain; for the fibro-vascular cords are too degraded to furnish assistance. In *Equisetum* there is a perfect transition; collenchyma being at the angles in the aërial stems, it gradually decreases in quantity below the surface of the water, and finally disappears altogether, apparently just in proportion as the mechanical strains to be met diminish.

The endoderm is generally much the same in both, though the suberised "folds" tend to disappear in the aërial, while they are very pronounced in the aquatic stem, as occurs also in *Equisetum* and *Mentha*.

The fibro-vascular cords are continued from the aërial to the aquatic portions, but *tend* to degenerate, and vanish only if a plant be naturally and always absolutely submerged.

M. Costantin observes that the fibro-vascular cords of amphibious plants preserve in the water the aërial organisation when their *bases only* are submerged; but it is sufficient to compel the plants to grow in deep water for the fibrous and vascular elements to become at once greatly reduced, and not infrequently do they vanish altogether, as in *Aldrovandia*, which has no longer any vessels in the internodes.

Perhaps no structure shows the effect of water in a more pronounced manner than the various degrees of degeneracy which the vascular system undergoes.

While the effects of the different media are clearly seen, it must be also noticed that different parts may vary even in the same medium. Thus the aquatic stem of *Trapa natans* is formed entirely of soft tissue, and cannot rise to the surface; but through an increase of the lacunæ of the stem and the inflation of the petioles of the upper leaves, the flowering stem is enabled to rise so as to produce its flowers in the air. Hence the cortex forms four or five circles of

large lacunæ in the upper part of the stem, there being only
two in the lower part in deep water.

Again, Mr. A. Fryer,[1] in describing certain species of
Potamogeton, says of *P. varians*, Morong. (in Herb. ined.):
"Stem springing from a tuberous root-stock, slender, usually
simple below, with a few branches above the middle, *not
divided into secondary* branchlets; or in shallow water with
a few branches from the base, each springing from the axil
of a persistent leaf, and then *rarely with very short secondary
branchlets.*"

It will be seen hereafter that leaves also vary greatly
according to the depth of the water in which they occur
even on the same plant.

M. Ch. Martins discusses the synonyms of *Jussiæa repens*,
L., naming seventeen in all, and shows that these arise in
accordance with the environment in which they grow; *e.g.*,
submerged, on wet soil, and in dry situations:—"De tels
changements dans les conditions d'existence amènent des
variations de forme qui ont conduit les botanistes à voir des
espèces différentes dans de simples modifications d'un seul et
même type végétal."[2]

M. Bary calls attention to a special feature characteristic
of the stems of aquatic plants, whether endogenous or exogenous, and therefore one of adaptation and not affinity, in
that they are provided with an axile bundle; a feature
which tends to an approximation to root structure, and so
becomes indicative of degradation. The reader is referred to
his work for the enumeration of many aquatic plants provided
with this peculiarity.[3]

---

[1] *Journ. of Bot.*, vol. xxvii. 1889, p. 33.

[2] *Mémoire sur les Racines aérifères ou Vessies natatoires des Espèces
aquatiques du Genre Jussiæa*, par Ch. Martins, p. 11.

[3] *Comp. Anat.*, &c., pp. 277, 340.

EXPERIMENTAL EVIDENCE OF THE EFFECTS OF WATER UPON
THE STEMS OF TERRESTRIAL PLANTS.—M. Costantin and others,
including myself, have grown ordinary terrestrial plants in
water with the following results.[1] The persistence or modification of the epidermis may occur. Thus M. Costantin
found that no change was produced in *Vicia sativa* on the
stems maintained in water, while their length had become
tripled. On the other hand, M. Lewakoffski[2] found that in
Epilobium hirsutum, Lycopus europœus, and in two species of
Lythrum, the epidermis of the stem has disappeared very
soon from the submerged plants. As a similar change is very
pronounced in the epidermis of leaves, the conclusion one
would arrive at is, that the absence of a true aërial epidermis
with many stomata is the direct effect of the medium; but
that when normally terrestrial plants are made to grow in
water, the change is not always nor equally produced, but
that hereditary effects are too powerful in highly developed
plants to lose their characteristic features all at once. On
the other hand, plants like *Ranunculus heterophyllus* and
Callitriche, the different leaves of which are continually being
either entirely submerged or else floating, or even entirely
in air, the power to develop an epidermis, with stomata or
not, is naturally accommodative, and responds immediately to
the external medium in which the individual leaf happens
to be.

With regard to the thickness of the cortex, M. Costantin did
not find any appreciable difference in the case of *Phaseolus
vulgaris, Vicia sativa, Lupinus albus*, and *Ricinus communis*.

---

[1] Adapted from M. Costantin's paper, *Ann. des Sci. Nat. Bot.*, 6 Sér.
xix. 1884, p. 301.

[2] *Ueber den Einfluss des Wassers auf das Wachsthum der Stengel und
Wurzeln einiger Pflanzen. Mem. de l'Acad. de Kazan*, 1873, No. 6. Ab-
stract in *Just. Botan. Jahresb.*, 1873, p. 594.

On the other hand, M. Lewakoffski found, by making transverse sections at the same height on the stems of the same species grown in water and on land, that the aquatic stem produced between the cambium and the cortical parenchyma two series of translucent cells without chlorophyll, three or four times longer than broad, a series which did not exist in the terrestrial plant. This difference also increases with age.

Below the level of the water these two series of cells become a thick tissue provided with lacunæ.

The spongy aëriferous roots of *Jussiæa repens* and other species are, like canal-bearing stems of other aquatic plants, the actual production of the aquatic medium, for they cease to be formed as soon as the stem rises into the air, or when the stolon is cultivated in soil. If, however, in the latter case, the stolon be allowed to extend itself in water, the spongy roots immediately reappear. "Un *Jussiæa* cultivé dans un terrain sec ne pousse des racines caulinaires que dans la portion inférieure de la tige en contact avec le sol, qui conserve toujours un peu d'humidité après les pluies ; jamais il ne se développe de racines aérifères."[1]

The fibro-vascular system, as stated, is always more or less degenerate in aquatic plants. As in etiolated, so with submerged stems, one finds in both a like retardation in the appearance of the liber fibres, and a like arrest in the development of the vascular system. Thus, while there is no liber in the submerged stem of the castor-oil plant, they are well formed in the aërial stem. M. Costantin found similar differences, but less accentuated, in the Lupin. The diminution of the number of vessels is very uniform. Thus in *Vicia sativa* the middle of the aërial stem had 47, that of the aquatic only 38. The bottom of the former had 66, that of the

[1] M. Martins (*op. cit.*) describes the "land form" as being very different from the "water form."

latter 46. *Ricinus communis* had similarly 26 and 21 against
10 and 19 respectively; while *Faba vulgaris* growing on land
had 5 at the sides and 36 at the angles. These numbers
were reduced to 2 and 15, in corresponding positions, in the
aquatic stem.

As the preceding results from experiments exactly tally with
the structure of normally aquatic plants, the conclusion is
inevitable that this regular and persistent reduction in the
number of vessels is a direct result of the effects of water
upon submerged stems.

M. Costantin sums up his results as follows:—"The
aquatic medium determines the formation of cortical or
medullary lacunæ, and it arrests the development of the vascular and fibrous tissues."

AQUATIC PLANTS GROWN ON LAND IN AIR.—In the preceding section I have considered the effects of the medium
upon the structure of normally terrestrial and aërial plants
when grown in water. We will now see that the converse
effects tend to appear when aquatic plants are grown on
land.

There are numerous plants which are frequently "amphibious," living submerged entirely, or in part with floating
leaves, and also on the mud, or even dry soil, when the water
has disappeared. Such are *Ranunculus heterophyllus*, *Peplis
Portula*, species of *Potamogeton*, *Callitriche*, *Myriophyllum*,
Bidens, &c. In comparing the histological structures of the
two forms, one finds profound differences; yet there is no
question of their being derived from one and the same source
respectively. That this is the case is proved by taking the
water form and growing it experimentally on land, or the
land form and growing it in water.

M. Costantin selected plants of the aquatic form of *Peplis
Portula*, and grew one in water and the other on land. The

former, as is usual with aquatic forms, had elongated internodes, while in the other they were short. In both stems
the cortical parenchyma was hollowed out with four large
lacunæ. In both they were mainly the same size, but while
the septa remained homogeneous in the land form, they were
hollowed into secondary lacunæ in the aquatic.

Similar changes occurred in *Callitriche stagnalis*, *Nasturtium
officinale*, and *Myosotis palustris*. In *Callitriche*, while the
intercellular spaces increase much in size, the cortical cells
become rounded in the aquatic form, instead of becoming
quadrangular, as in the land form.

"Thus," adds M. Costantin, "the aquatic medium *determines* the increase of the cortical lacunæ of the stem; it is
the result which comparative anatomy leads one to foresee,
but which experiment alone could prove. These variations,
though slight, are not the less interesting, for they show
that the duration of the existence in air has no need to be
prolonged before the differences show themselves. Experiments, moreover, prove that the lacunæ are still persistent
when the plant is grown in an aërial medium; the plant,
therefore, notwithstanding the new conditions of its environment, retains the character of its aquatic life, although they
are less pronounced." It may be added that similar results
accrue from heredity.

The next point to notice is that the number of vessels
increase when an aquatic plant is grown on land. Thus,
in *Peplis Portula* the corresponding numbers were 25 and
53; in *Callitriche*, 4 and 12; in *Nasturtium*, 18 and 57;
to which I can add *Bidens cernua*, which has isolated
groups in the aquatic form, but a complete circle of fibro-
vascular cords in the land form. Moreover, the degradations
so characteristic of the aquatic all tend to disappear in the
land form.

M. de Bary [1] divided vessels into two categories—imperfect and rudimentary, to which may be added a total absence or arrest of all trace of them, a lacuna occupying the position. Plenty of illustrations of these conditions may be seen, e.g., in the plates in M. Chatin's work; but if a few common water-plants be dissected, the reader will soon discover ample evidence of this deteriorating effect of growth in water.

While the vascular system at once begins to "improve," so do collenchyma and liber fibres to appear. The interpretation is, that as the stems require means to support themselves in air, these tissues are developed to meet the strain to keep them erect. [2]

An increase of the central cylinder accompanies the development of the vascular system, and shows that the central vascular cord is a structure analogous to that of terrestrial Exogens. M. Costantin's figure of *Peplis Portula* shows that the aquatic medium, by reducing on the one hand, the diameter of the pith and of the central cylinder, by arresting the development of the vessels, determines the formation of a central body, which, by its minuteness and the feeble importance of the vascular system, has been regarded as a single vascular cord. The aquatic stem of *Peplis*, in its totality, recalls absolutely the structure of the central system of many stems of *Primulaceæ*, *Scrophularineæ*, &c. One can therefore pass by a series of transitions from the structure of the "body" which is found in the centre of certain aquatic stems to the normal type of a fibro-vascular cylinder, surrounded by an endoderm, and containing medullary tissue within it.

There is another feature in certain stems which would

---

[1] *Vergleichende Anatomie*, p. 381 seq.

[2] The reader is referred to chapter xi. for a full discussion of adaptations to mechanical strains.

'seem to be due to the effect of water, judging at least by its appearance in aquatic or sub-aquatic plants. It is called an *astélique* condition by Van Tieghem, who has shown that in several horse-tails, *Equisetum limosum*, *E. littorale*, &c., in *Ophioglossum*, and in certain Exogens, *Nymphœaceœ*, *Ranunculus Lingua*, *R. aquatilis*, &c., and of Endogens in *Hydrocharis*, *Limnocharis*, &c., the stem is characterised by the absence of a true central cylinder or *stèle*. They are therefore *astélique*. Each libero - ligneous cord is in fact plunged directly into a parenchyma which is continuous from the periphery to the centre; a layer of which bordering each cord is developed in a *special* endoderm together with its own pericycle around it.[1]

One knows, on the other hand, that the pericycle is by definition the part of the conjunctive tissue of the central cylinder which lies exterior to the fibro-vascular cords. In the *astélique* structure there is, therefore, no true central cylinder; so that there would be neither pericycle nor pith nor medullary rays.

M. van Tieghem gives the name *peridesme* to the layer of tissue which in the *astélique* structure surrounds as a particular endoderm the liber and the wood of each fibro-vascular cord.[2]

M. Costantin appears to have observed this peculiarity in 1884, for he remarks :—" L'endoderme de la tige florale (of *Ranunculus heterophyllus*) entoure complètement chaque faisceau, au lieu de contourner tout le cylindre central, comme cela a lieu pour la tige submergée."[3]

THE COMPARATIVE ANATOMY OF AQUATIC AND TERRESTRIAL SUBTERRANEAN STEMS.—Commencing with cortical lacuna,

---

[1] *Traité de Botanique*, p. 764.

[2] *Remarques sur la Structure de la Tige des Prêles*. *Journ. de Bot.*, No. 21, 1890.

[3] *Ann. des Sci. Nat.*, 1884, 6 Sér. tom. xix. p. 318.

M. Costantin shows that those which are so characteristic of stems surrounded by water are retained in aquatic subterranean regions though reduced in size. In fact, the cortex of one and the same stem may present three different aspects, in the aërial, aquatic, and subterranean regions respectively. Thus, *e.g.*, in *Veronica scutellata* in the first region, the cortex is feeble and the lacunæ numerous; in the submerged part, the volume increases as the lacunæ become very large; while in the subterranean portion the lacunæ again diminish, but are not so small as in the aërial part. The above is equally true for other plants.

He found that by burying the aërial stems of *Ranunculus heterophyllus* at the bottom of the water, the cortex at once became thicker. This fact, he adds, proves that the increase of the cortical parenchyma in the subterranean parts exists for aquatic as well as for terrestrial plants. He concludes with the words :—"One observes, therefore, in the terrestrial parts of aquatic plants, the ordinary increase of the cortex; this region becomes hollowed, however, with lacunæ by the action of the medium being partly aquatic in which the rhizomes grow."

With regard to a suberous layer, a corky surface rapidly appears on subterranean stems in dry soils. This also appears in aquatic subterranean stems, but much modified. Sometimes it is only the epidermis, as in *Myriophyllum*, &c., which becomes suberified. The importance of this protecting layer is therefore less in water than in rhizomes of terrestrial plants. It is very likely, he observes, that the very humid soil in which these rhizomes grow offers less resistance to their growth, so that the external layers are less frequently torn.

Collenchyma disappears nearly constantly in subterranean stems after a longer or shorter sojourn in the soil. Aquatic plants undergo equally this change. Thus a subterranean stem of *Helosciadum inundatum*, which was much older than the aquatic stem, did not present collenchyma in the cortex, while the latter had it in front of the cords.

With regard to the endoderm, the middle walls are slightly suberified; the expansion of the wall produces a fold, which gives rise (according to Schwendener[1]) to the characteristic black spot. In the rhizome of *Helosciadum* these spots do not occur, although they are present in the aquatic stem. In other stems they may occur in both, as of *Myriophyllum*, or in neither, as of *Veronica*. Suberine is, however, produced with difficulty in aquatic stems generally, either in the external layers or on the walls of the endoderm.

M. Costantin thus sums up his observations : " After having established experimentally how the sojourn of a stem in water, in air, or in earth modifies it, I have looked to see how the preceding modifications occur upon one and the same axis divided into three regions plunged into three different media.

" The comparison of aquatic with subterranean stems shows, for the latter, that the lacunæ are reduced in size ; the vascular system is a little more developed ; the fibres and collenchyma disappear nearly completely ; the peripheric layers are suberified, and the endoderm is more differentiated."

I will conclude this section with a brief comparison between the anatomical details of *Bidens cernua* growing in water and on hardened mud, which I have had an opportunity of observing. M. Costantin has also examined the same plant. In his figures, he shows that in the subterranean parts the large wedge-shaped lacunæ have entirely disappeared, nothing but little, quadrangular interspaces remaining. In my speci-

---

[1] *Die Schutzscheiden und ihre Verstärkungen* (*Abhandl. der K. Akad. der Wissensch. zu Berlin*, 1882).

mens the lacunæ were present, but greatly reduced in size. In M. Costantin's case the xylem is isolated, and forms a more or less quadrangular mass in the very centre of the root, up the axis, the cells being arranged in no order. In mine, there was a perfect and dense cylinder of wood of radiating fibres with scattered vessels, surrounding a central pith with a circular lacuna.

The aquatic and terrestrial habits, however, were correlated with other differences respectively. Thus the structure of the basal and creeping part of the stem, from which adventitious roots descend, showed similar differences to those of the roots. In the case of the aquatic plant the fibro-vascular cords were separated into wedge-shaped masses. In the terrestrial they formed a continuous and compact cylinder. The cortical lacunæ also were smaller than in the aquatic plant, while the epidermis was composed of square cells in the land form, and narrow elongated ones [1] in the corresponding place in the aquatic.

Similarly, in the aërial parts, the stem was greener and broader than in the land form, tapering upwards; while in the latter it was more cylindrical. In the aquatic, there was a compact medulla, with wedge-shaped isolated cords or xylem without sclerenchyma, and more numerous cortical lacunæ. In the land form, each cord was provided with an outer dense mass of pericycular sclerenchyma. Lastly, a very large lacuna formed by laceration occurred in the middle of the pith.

The above details will be sufficient to show how profoundly the medium affects a plant according as it grows in water or on dry ground.

LEAVES OF AQUATIC PLANTS, FOLIAR DIMORPHISM.—The aërial and floating leaves, when present on the same aquatic

---

[1] This difference is perhaps correlated with a reduced tension in the epidermal layers.

plant, generally differ very greatly in form, and always in structure, from the submerged leaves. In *Ranunculus heterophyllus, Cabomba aquatica, Trapa natans*, &c., the floating leaves are more or less rounded, with an entire or crenated margin; while the submerged ones have dissected and filiform segments. In *Nymphœa* the floating and submerged leaves are alike in form but different in structure. In *Hippuris* and *Callitriche* the aërial and floating leaves are linear and short in the former, round in the latter; while the submerged leaves of both, as well as those of *Lobelia Dortmanna, Limosella aquatica*, and *Littorella lacustris*, are ribbon-like or linear, recalling the prevailing form of submerged leaves of Endogens.

In all cases the submerged leaves are of a more delicate texture, more or less translucent, and of a brighter green colour than the others.

With regard to the anatomical structure of a submerged leaf, it shows degradation in every part. Thus, the epidermal cells of *Hippuris* completely alter their shape, becoming elongated with straight walls, the cuticle disappearing, and there are no stomata.[1] The mesophyll is greatly reduced in quantity, as also are the chlorophyll grains, while the lacunæ enlarge, the phloëm and liber being much reduced. The vessels also diminish in number to one quarter of that in the aërial leaf; the thickness of the submerged leaf being less than one-half that of the other.

In *Ranunculus heterophyllus*, the epidermis of the submerged leaf forms the superficial layer of the mesophyll containing chlorophyll, its inner walls not being parallel to the surface,

---

[1] The reader is referred to De Bary's *Comp. Anat.*, &c., p. 49, for an account of "the occurrence and distribution of air-pores yielding many remarkable examples of the change of structure by direct, often individual, adaptations.

but fitting between the angles of the subjacent cells. There is a similar reduction in all the interior elements.

Very pronounced differences occur between the leaves of plants of the same species growing in deep and shallow water respectively. Thus *Isoetes lacustris*, var. *stricta*, is a result of its growing in shallow places.; while *I. lacustris*, var. *elatior*, frequents much greater depths.[1]

Sagittaria sagittifolia is interesting as furnishing transitions from the .submerged, purely ribbon-like form to the aërial sagittate blade. In deep water it produces the former only ; nearer the surface the ends of the leaves assume a spathulate or sub-elliptic form ; the next type is an elongated hastate. ; and finally the sagittate form is attained.

The most interesting family of plants which illustrates this feature is the *Nymphœaceœ*. It was long doubted whether they should be classed as Exogens or Endogens ; for they possess so many features characteristic of the latter · class. These features, however, are simply adaptive to water, but have become hereditary and typical of Endogens, whether aquatic or not.

With regard to the leaves, the first formed are arrested as linear phyllodes; and a close comparison may be made, *e.g.*, between the foliage of *Victoria regia* and that of *Sagittaria sagittifolia*. Thus, the first leaf in a *Victoria* seedling is a petiole without any blade ; the second has a lanceolate limb ; the third is hastate ; the fourth sagittate-peltate ; the subsequent ones being orbicular-peltate.

Sagittaria has ribbon-like foliage when growing in deep water, and is then known as the variety *Vallisneriifolia*, Casson and Germ.; the following leaves are, as stated, spathulate, hastate, and sagittate. The sagittate-peltate is attained by the

---

[1] Fliche, *Les Isoetes des Vosges*, 1879.

genera *Caladium* and *Alocasia*, and the orbicular by *Hydrocharis* of Endogens.[1]

A cause may be suggested for the origin of the hastate and sagittate types of submerged leaves, as follows :—As long as the water is more or less deep and poorly illuminated, a tendency to elongate the phyllode, like a stem in etiolation, exists ; but as light increases in shallower water, an opposite effect takes place, namely, an arrest of the elongation sets in. Growth, however, continues, and this can only find relief in some lateral expansion. In many cases this takes the form of an elliptical blade, as in *Potamogeton natans*, &c.; but if the lateral growth is more limited in extent, it appears as slight bulgings, which give rise to the hastate form. By increased lateral growth it passes into the sagittate, the points necessarily turning downwards, as upward growth would be checked, just as the central terminal growth is, by light. Two illustrative cases support the above view.   M. Costantin describes an instance in which the hastate form of *Sagittaria* was just commencing to be formed, when the water in which it was growing became suddenly deepened. The leaf continued to grow, but now recommenced elongating its apex as before, when it was solely ribbon-like.[2] A specimen in my own collection has a hastate blade, but all three points are ribbon-like and elongated.

The conclusion appears inevitable that these above-described forms are produced in response to the conditions of an increasing amount of light, which acts in an arresting way upon the plant as the leaves are developed nearer and nearer to the surface.

---

[1] For further details the reader is referred to the paper "On the Origin of Endogens" (*supra*, p. 149).

[2] *Etudes sur les Feuilles des Plantes aquatiques. Ann. des Sci. Nat.*, Sér. 7, tom. iii. Pl. v. fig. 37.

Hereditary influences now come into play ; for the ultimate forms of the leaves of aquatic plants begin to be, foreshadowed in the bud at the bottom of the water in anticipation of the conditions to which they will be respectively suitable. This may be well seen, *e.g.*, by growing *Ranunculus heterophyllus* in a bowl of water. After producing the submerged dissected leaves, the floating form is developed below, and the petioles elongate more or less according to the depth of the water till the blades reach and float on the surface. So strong is this hereditary force, that when seeds of this plant are sown in earth, the plant still pursues the same course, developing a certain number of dissected leaves, but anatomically of the aërial type, and subsequently leaves of the floating type, suggestive of an " instinct at fault." The whole plant, however, is now in perfect adaptation to its terrestrial and aërial environment.

Just as the leaves of *Ranunculus heterophyllus* can be thus altered at will, so, as remarked in the case of *Sagittaria*, a sudden elevation of the water will change the form of a developing leaf at once. Thus, not only, as described, if an arrow-headed leaf is in course of development and be suddenly made to grow in deeper water, the " arrow " becomes elongated or "linear-sagittate," but at the same time the following leaves, which would have been sagittate, now remain spathulate. A permanent increase in the depth of water, therefore, induces a retrogression in the development.

It may be added that any cause which arrests the vigour of a plant may bring about a similar retrogression ; thus if the differentiated leaves of *Alisma* be cut away, the subsequent leaves are ribbon-like.

There are other anatomical details due to the aquatic medium, such as the reduction of hair on submerged leaves of *Epilobium hirsutum, Polygonum amphibium,* and *Ranunculus acris,* &c. ; the arrest of sclerenchymatous structures and a reduction of the supportive system; but as these have already been alluded to in submerged stems, it need only ·be added that exactly the same procedure takes place in submerged leaves.

With regard to floating leaves, the rounded form is very characteristic, as in the exogenous *Nymphæaceæ, Cabomba, Limnanthemum,* and in the endogenous *Hydrocharis.* As these plants occur in widely different orders of Phanerogams, one would on à *priori* grounds infer that the form was in some way in adaptation to their environment. Now we are indebted to Mr. W. P. Hiern for having investigated this matter mathematically, and he has arrived at the conclusion that, on the supposition that "the marginal vigour of growth is the same at all points,"—a reasonable one, as the margin develops symmetrically and forms an approximate circle,— the leaf develops in adaptation to the strains to which it is submitted in running water. Mr. Hiern adds the following remark, which is quite in keeping with other phenomena in plants :—"It is a tenable hypothesis, and by no means improbable, that during much or most of the time when actual growth is taking place, and when the velocity of the current is subject to many and various vicissitudes, the plant has the power of adapting its growing efforts to the circumstances just necessary for its development. . . . The theory discusses the forms which floating leaves would find mechanically suitable for their growth and maintenance, in order that they might dwell free from unnecessary strains and wrenches, and under an equal distribution of their power of growth, which, as we know, is capable of exerting considerable force under compulsion, but is in general slow and steady." [1]

Everything tends to support Mr. Hiern's view ; and I think

[1] "A Theory of the Forms of Floating Leaves in certain Plants," by W. P. Hiern, M.A. *Proc. of the Cam. Phil. Soc.,* October 1872. Jönsson (*Ber. d. deut. Bot. Ges.,* i. 1883) has observed that the direction of growth of

that we may add that the varieties of dissected foliage of *Ranunculus heterophyllus* may be traced to analogous causes. Thus, while the form *fluitans*, with long parallel segments, is characteristic of rapid streams, *R. circinatus*, with circular-arranged segments, frequents still waters.

CHARACTERISTIC FEATURES AND ADAPTATIONS OF AQUATIC LEAVES.—Plants which have their leaves normally either all submerged or with some floating, exhibit quite as marked peculiarities, both morphologically and histologically, in these organs as in stems and roots.

They take generally, as described above, one of two forms when growing entirely below the surface : they are either ribbon-like or finely dissected. The former prevails in Endogens, the latter in Exogens ; though the submerged leaves of *Hippuris*, *Lobelia Dortmanna*, and some others, resemble the endogenous type.

My contention is that all the forms of submerged leaves, as well as the floating, are the direct outcome of the conditions under which they grow.

I propose making a brief resumé, as before, from M. Costantin's paper,[1] and then supplementing it with my own and others' observations.

1. *Ribbon-like Leaves.*—These are met with in the greater part of endogenous aquatic plants. Under the action of water these leaves elongate to a much greater length than do the leaves in air. Thus M. Costantin shows by figures how the

plant-organs is affected when they are exposed to the influence of a current of water ; he designates the induced phenomenon by the term *Rheotropism.* Vines, " Phys. of Plants," p. 473. See also Behrens, *Jahresb. Nat. Ges.,* Elberfeld, 1880 ; *Kosmos,* vii. (1880), pp. 466–471.

See also *Observations sur les Conditions de Développement des Feuilles nageantes. Ass. fr. pour l'Av. des Sci.,* 1881, *Congrès d'Alger, Bull. de la Soc. Bot. de Fr.,* 1882, p. 225.

[1] *Etudes sur les Feuilles des Plantes aquatiques. Ann. des Sci. Nat.,* Sér. 7, 1886, tom. iii. p. 94.

leaves of *Sagittaria* when deeply submerged can reach more than six feet in length. They can, however, be developed in air, when, instead of being long, soft, and flexible, they are short, firm, and erect, though still retaining the ribbon-like form. The same fact may be noticed in *Scirpus lacustris* and *Sparganium minimum.* In the case of *Hippuris*, M. Costantin changed the form at will by transplanting an aquatic plant on to land and *vice versâ :* all the leaves produced under water were long, undulated, and delicate ; whereas those in air were short, erect, and firm.

2. *Capillary Leaves.*—Many observers have recorded the fact, that while the capillary form is characteristic of the submerged leaves of Exogens, as of *Ranunculus heterophyllus* and others, when the shoots reach the air, or the water dries up and the plants become terrestrial, the new leaves generally remain capillary, but are altered considerably both in form and structure. Thus the segments become less numerous in the air, and the ramifications are shorter, broader, and thicker. A transverse section shows an oval outline, whereas that of an aquatic segment is circular. Nature frequently performs this experiment, while several botanists as well as myself[1]

---

[1] I collected seeds from a form very near *R. Baudotii*, Good., growing in shallow rain-water pools in the rocks in Malta. They grew in water to much larger plants in England, and more like our typical *R. heterophyllus*, during the summer of 1894. But from having been annuals in Malta—as the pools are always dried up by August—my plants have assumed the character of "perennials," and are still flourishing (Feb. 9, 1895), having been frozen over more than once. A curious alteration has taken place in the form of the "floating" leaves. In Malta they are cuneate at the base, with a rounded but crenated margin on the distal end. They are now all deeply pinnatifid, with flat; ribbon-like segments. Moreover, they are more inclined to be partially or entirely under water, but close to, rather than actually and entirely upon, the surface.

May 10*th.*—The typical floating form has reappeared, but is larger than in Malta.

have raised terrestrial plants from seed collected from aquatic plants, when the same phenomena appear.[1] In my own case, the plants, after producing a certain number of dissected leaves of the aërial type, developed others of the floating form, although it was in air. The stomata were as usual on the upper side, but a few made their appearance below.

In this case was seen very neatly the influences of the environment in combination with heredity; for by transferring plants backwards and forwards from water to air and *vice versâ*, the previously formed dissected leaves perished in both cases, while new ones were always and at once formed in adaptation to the new environment respectively.

Myriophyllum[2] furnishes similar phenomena, as I have myself proved. M. Costantin adds a third illustration in *Œnanthe Phellandrium*. The aërial leaves of this plant are very much dissected, but their structure remains firm, and their tint a pronounced green. The aquatic leaves are, on the contrary, very thin, and of a pale green colour;[3] the simple dentitions of the aërial leaf become deep incisions, and the teeth of the filaments fine and narrow in the aquatic form.

3. *Leaves with a Large and Thin Limb.*—Such are the submerged leaves of *Nuphar luteum*. These leaves are often at the exterior of the plant, and are of slight thickness and remarkably translucent; the colour is of a bright green, and

---

[1] M. Askenay (*Bot. Zeit.*, 1870) made plants germinate. M. Mer (*Bull. de la Soc. Bot.*, 1880, p. 50) verified the experiment.

[2] Observed by M. Schenck, *Die Biologie der Wasser-Gewächse*, 1885, p. 22.

[3] Hooker observes a similar difference between the aquatic and terrestrial species of *Myosotis* ("Student's Flora"). Plants of *Ranunculus acris* raised from seed in water show similar differences, varying only in degree from those raised on land.

their feeble consistence allows them to wave gently in the water. *Potamogeton lucens* is a similar type.[1]

4. *Intermediate Cases.*—M. Costantin observes that the study of some of the *Podostemaceœ* seems to justify the preceding views. One can infer from a comparison of the forms of leaves of certain species of this strange family how successive transformations have occurred from an entire to a dissected leaf. He illustrates a leaf of *Mourera fluviatilis* in which the margin is partially dissected. It is thin and transparent, being cut at the periphery, as if one had removed all the tissue which is between the extreme ends of the veins. From this stage one cản pass through other species to those in a completely capillary condition.[2]

In Endogens an analogous arrest of intra-fascicular parenchyma is seen in *Ouvirandra fenestralis*, and in a less degree in some submerged leaves of species of *Potamogeton*.

Several observers have noted what I have found to be the case with *Ranunculus heterophyllus*—that aërial leaves perish under water, and aquatic leaves perish in air. Thus, M. Rozer[3] records this as occurring with *Nuphar luteum*, while M. Mer[4]

---

[1] As Phanerogams supply ample material for proving the effect of water, I have not alluded much to Cryptogams. An interesting case, however, has been described by K. Giesenhagen in a paper *Ueber hygrophile Farne* (Flora, 1892, p. 157), in which *Asplenium obtusifolium*, L., var. *aquaticum*, is mentioned as more or less approximating the *Hymenophyllaceæ*; thereby indicating the probability that the so-called "filmy ferns" owe their simplicity to degradation from a similar cause.

[2] I would refer the reader to Professor Eug. Warming's treatise on the *Podostomaceæ* (published 1881, 1882, 1888, and completed in 1891, with numerous plates and illustrations in the text) for further details on the remarkable structure of the plants of this family.

[3] *Flore de la Côte-d'Or, Nymphéacées.*

[4] *Des Effets de l'Eau sur les Feuilles aquatiques. Bull. de la Soc. Bot. de Fr.*, 1878, p. 89.

adds that the same plant has coriaceous leaves when they stand out completely into the air.

These differences do not always occur on the same plant, for some species appear to have become permanently submerged, and can only live entirely under water. Thus I found that *Ranunculus circinatus* and *Elodea canadensis* are in this condition; and, to judge from their appearance, it is probable that the *Podostomaceæ*, like many *Algæ*, have arrived at this advanced stage of degradation, so that they cannot resist the slightest desiccation without fatal injury.

The rapid adaptation to a new medium is well seen when a half-formed floating leaf is submerged; for it is at once arrested, and then begins to readapt itself to water. This may be readily seen in *Ranunculus heterophyllus* and *Sagittaria*, as already described. An analogous case occurs in the leaves of *Callitriche*, in which submerged leaves tend to assume the ribbon-like form, the aërial being oval.

These experiments show that when a leaf is quite adult, the change of environment kills it; but when it is in course of its development, it can then change its adaptation and fit itself for the new environment.

M. Mer is another botanist who has studied the structure of aquatic plants.[1]

In the first paper referred to below, he gives a minute description of the morphology and anatomy of the leaves of *Ranunculus aquatilis* (*heterophyllus*) and *Littorella lacustris* when growing on land and in water, as well as of the sub-

[1] *Des Modifications de Forme et de Structure que subissent les Plantes suivant qu'elles végètent à l'Air ou sous l'Eau. Bull. de la Soc. Bot. de Fr.*, 1880, p. 50.

Des Causes qui modifient la Structure de certaines Plantes aquatiques végétant dans l'Eau. Bull. de la Soc. Bot. de Fr., 1880, p. 194. See also his later contributions in subsequent years.

merged and floating leaves of *Potamogeton natans*. Having examined several plants in the two conditions, he was enabled to summarise the differences as follows :—The stems, petioles, and sessile leaves of aquatic forms are generally of greater length, the breadth being sometimes greater (*L. lacustris, Carex ampullacea*), sometimes less (*R. aquatilis, R. flammula, Callitriche, Scirpus*). The chlorophyllous cells are less abundant and the grains fewer in quantity. The fibro-vascular cords are less developed. The vessels are less numerous, their dimensions narrower, their walls more delicate. The epidermal cells are more elongated, and with rectilinear outlines, and the walls are thinner. Stomata and hairs are rare. In some species, as *R. aquatilis* and *Myriophyllum alterniflorum*, the differences in the form of the leaves are still more pronounced. Not only do they become shorter when developed in air, but they are flatter and tend to develop a lamina. The dimensions of the limb of the aquatic form are more slender, till they nearly disappear, as in *Potamogeton natans*.

M. Mer has also noticed a very close correspondence between submerged organs and those of terrestrial plants growing in places more or less devoid of light, or etiolated. This is seen in the elongation of the stems and in the ribbon-like leaves of submerged Endogens. These are really phyllodes. When *Myriophyllum* develops dissected leaves in air, they exactly correspond with those of *Ranunculus aquatilis ;* but when the plants were subsequently placed in weak light, the newly developed branches and leaves became intermediate in character between those of aërial and aquatic forms. The plants had thus *three* different structures on the same branches.

When aquatic and terrestrial forms were grown under a bell-glass in light, the new shoots of the aërial parts approximated the aquatic, and those of the aquatic now growing in air approximated the aërial in form. Both forms approached the usual results of etiolation.

M. Mer explains these results as follows :—The elongation of the axis and petioles in obscurity, with an arrest of blades, is attributed to the former using up the materials intended for the latter; while in the blades the cells develop less chlorophyll, consequently transpiration and assimilation are both checked. If one holds under water a young floating leaf of *R. aquatilis*, the development of the limb is at once checked,—just as M. Costantin proved in the case of *Sagittaria*,—while that of the petiole is increased, and it elongates immoderately.

Conversely, as soon as the limb comes to the surface it enlarges, and the petiole ceases to grow.

If one suppresses the limb, the petiole elongates less vigorously, and stops when it has consumed the starch which it enclosed. The limb is then necessary to draw this substance into the petiole, but it only uses it completely itself when it is subject to a sufficient transpiration.[1]

M. Mer thus writes on the effects of etiolation : [2]—

" The inferior internodes and petioles become longer, because their tissues are subject to less tension than in the light. The limbs and the superior internodes are shorter at first, because the petioles and the internodes (inferior) obtain nourishment which is always limited ; because subsequently the limbs, in the absence of light, only possess a feeble attractive power for water and plastic matters ; and finally, because they cannot acquire their normal dimensions when they do not assimilate."

---

[1] *Loc. cit.*, p. 190.
[2] *Recherches sur les Anomalies de Dimension des Entre-nœuds et des Feuilles étiolées*, par M. Emile Mer. *Bull. de la Soc. Bot. de Fr.*, 1875, p. 190.

Hence can be accounted for the elongation of leaves with short petioles in darkness.

Experiments with ordinary terrestrial plants when cultivated in water exhibit analogous features. Thus M. Costantin grew several species, as *Medicago minima*, *Lysimachia nummularia*, &c., under water. In all cases the effect is that the blades of the leaves are smaller than those in air. They are much thinner and more translucent than are the aërial leaves.

A study of the anatomical structure of closely related plants, such as grasses, in connection with their environment, has been made by Pfitzer,[1] and referred to by De Bary,[2] who recommends a careful investigation as to the "finer gradations of the distribution [of stomata, to see how far they] are directly caused by the mode of life and condition of vegetation." He continues: "Pfitzer has obtained the following result for a large number of indigenous grasses: that for these plants the number and distribution of the air-pores, together with the form of the surface and internal structure of the whole leaf, stand pretty generally in definite relation to the wetness of the locality." He then enumerates the differences obtaining in several species, grasses of wet localities having flat blades and stomata equally numerous on both sides. On the other hand, as described above, almost all grasses inhabiting very dry localities, the blades have longitudinal furrows, the stomata being within the furrows, and mainly on the upper side.[3]

Since the preceding was penned, a note by M. Oger[4] has appeared which thoroughly accords with the conclusions at which I have arrived. He grew the following plants in a wet soil and the same species in a dry one, other conditions being

[1] *Pringsheims Jahrb.*, vij.
[2] *Comp. Anat.*, &c., p. 50.
[3] See *supra*, p. 61.
[4] *Comptes Rendus*, cxv. p. 525.

equal:—*Lampsana communis, Sonchus asper, S. oleraceus, Mercurialis annua, Chenopodium album, Balsamina hortensis, Impatiens glanduligera,* and *Scrophularia aquatica.* He found that the plants growing in the moist soil not only became more luxuriant, throwing out more branches, &c., but their forms 'changed. Thus the later-formed leaves were more elongated and lanceolate in shape, while the lower or first-formed leaves chànged less. This, it may þe observed, agrees with *Ranunculus flammula* when grown from seed. The first leaves are cordate (hinting, perhaps, at an ancestral floating condition), but the subsequent ones in my cultivations were linear-lanceolate.

The internal structure of the stems changed in correlation with the morphological ones, in that the epidermis had the external walls less thick than is the case with plants growing in a very dry soil; and although the cortex did not differ much in thickness, M. Oger found that the central cylinder increased in diameter, as well as the central lacuna; for he found that the number of fibro-vascular bundles increased in quantity, while the diameter of the vessels was greater. The medullary sclerenchyma, when it exists, was found to be especially developed around the primary bundles. This seems to correspond with what commonly obtains in many endogenous stems. M. Oger concludes his note by observing that some of the modifications thus obtained agree with anatomical differences resembling those which one uses for classificatory purposes. One can thus obtain experimentally, he says, by means of humidity of the soil, *in a given species* modifications of structure of the same kind, though less pronounced, as those which serve to characterise allied species, some being adapted to a dry soil, others to a moist one.

CONCLUSION.—It would only weary the reader to multiply cases of adaptation in amphibious and aquatic plants, for the phenomena are the same in all. Enough has been said to prove by innumerable and invariable coincidences the existence of an adaptive or responsive power in plants; while the experimental evidence is conclusive. Degrees of degeneracy are seen to exist in different plants, which prove the corresponding existence of degrees in the reduced power of adaptation; as, *e.g.*, I have shown to be the case with *Ranunculus circinatus* and *Elodea canadensis*. From these we may at once conclude that the curious and extreme forms and greatly degraded state of the tissues found in the *Podostemaceœ* are simply the results of excessive aquatic degeneration. The fact that they mimic Lichens, Mosses, Hepaticæ, and Algæ affords the additional evidence that the form and structure of the leaves or thallus of these plants are equally the results of adaptation to a watery or moist habitat.

Prof. Eug. Warming, besides coming to the same conclusion that the vegetative structure of the members of the *Podostemaceœ* has been modified by the aquatic habit, has noticed that the young shoots have a dorsi-ventral structure. Such strongly appears to indicate an ancestral terrestrial life.

As bearing upon this subject, I may refer here to a paper by Mr. G. Massee,[1] in which he shows that *Algæ* and *Hepaticœ* vary in structure as one passes from deep water to a moist land surface. Thus *Delesseria sanguinea* and *Ulva latissima*, &c., perish as soon as they are out of water, while *Fuci*, &c., can resist desiccation for a longer period. "*Hepaticœ* form the transition from the aquatic to terrestrial vegetation, and it is in this family that we meet with marked modifications of structure, for the purpose of enabling the plants to exist under conditions so far removed from those in which their progenitors flourished."

As, however, we do not know anything about the ancestors

[1] On the Primary Causes of Variety in Plant Structure.' *Naturalist*, February 1884.

M

of existing sea-weeds, nor of those low-formed land plants, and how they arose, it would, I think, be as well, in speculating upon their evolutionary history, not to forget that the analogies supplied by existing aquatic phanerogams, and especially by the *Podostemaceæ*, would seem to indicate the possibility of *Algæ* being *degradations* from higher plants which were perhaps terrestrial, instead of their being the forerunners of the *Hepaticæ, Musci*, &c.

This observation applies, I believe, equally well to Endogens; for this group I take to have originated (as I have endeavoured to prove elsewhere[1]) from some early types of Exogens through an aquatic habit of life. The reader will perceive that the details of aquatic plants given in the present chapter, as well as those in the paper referred to below, are to a large extent generally applicable not only to existing aquatic endogenous plants, but to those which are now permanently terrestrial of that class. Lastly, the reader will bear in mind that classificatory characters, to a very large extent, have been based upon the forms of those organs of plants which we have here seen to have been developed solely by response to an aquatic medium. Darwinians will also observe that in no case are there any wasted, injurious, or ill-adapted variations; but that water induces all plants to vary alike, and to do so at once in harmony with itself. Natural selection, therefore, has no *raison d'être* whatever.

[1] A Theoretical Origin of Endogens from Exogens, through Self-Adaptation to an Aquatic Habit. *Journ. Linn. Soc. Bot.*, xxix. p. 485, 1893.

CHAPTER IX

ORIGIN OF SUBTERRANEAN STRUCTURES

(*Roots and Stems*)

INTERCHANGE BETWEEN ROOTS AND STEMS.—That roots and stems are structures differentiated from a common and fundamentally identical type, is obvious from such facts as the following:—Every detail in the histological elements of the two structures can, speaking generally, be paralleled one with another, allowing for the total arrest of one or more elements in certain cases. Stems can form roots when placed in the same conditions in which roots are formed, viz., darkness and moisture. Aërial roots can take on the functions of stems, and true roots formed underground can become stems and branches when exposed to air and light.

Now the fact I wish to emphasise is, that these differences between stems and roots are, as a rule, the direct results of the aërial and subterranean conditions of their normal existence respectively; and that when a subterranean root becomes superficial or aërial, it at once tends to · approximate the character of a stem; and if a normally aërial stem is made to grow underground, it in turn tends to acquire the characters of a true root. Not only does Nature often supply us with illustrations of these changes, but experiments distinctly verify the supposition. Thus, for example,[1] an old

---

[1] This occurred in the garden of the Vicarage at Ealing.

acacia' with a decaying trunk sent down an aërial root from the living part, about six feet from the ground. When it had been rooted in the soil for some time, it became detached above by the wind; the root then became a "stem," the upper part putting out foliage. This is quite analogous to the numerous roots of the banyan, which are to all intents and purposes equivalent to small trunks surrounding the parent tree.

When the roots of elms, hawthorns, horse-chestnuts, &c., get exposed on the sides of banks, they constantly send out a perfect forest of leafy shoots.

The following experiment, recorded by Dr. Lindley, will also illustrate this. A young willow-tree had its crown bent down to the ground; this was covered with earth, and soon emitted an abundance of roots. The true roots were then carefully removed from the soil and the stem inverted. The roots now became branches and emitted buds, and the tree grew ever afterwards upside down.

When the tissues are examined, they are found to alter more or less in correlation with their new positions. Thus M. Costantin[1] found that when a root is maintained in the light, the thickness of the cortex diminishes, while the central cylinder is, on the contrary, more developed; though the pith, according to Dr. Lindley,[2] may be still deficient.

Exactly the reverse results followed by growing a normally aërial stem underground. The endodermic punctations, so well marked in subterranean roots, become indistinct when they are grown in the air, and this membrane is often unrecognisable, just as it is in so many stems and branches, &c. Conversely, in the aërial roots of orchids and aroids, the

---

[1] *Influence du Milieu sur la Structure anatomique de la Racine. Bull. de la Soc. Bot. de Fr.*, xxxi. 1884, p. 25.

[2] Theory of Horticulture, p. 32.

endoderm is often difficult to detect; but the thick-walled layer called the endoderm in aërial roots of *Vanda*, &c., can be proved to be such, for its cells become punctated if the root be below the soil. All fibrous tissues are more developed in aërial structures, whether in the central cylinder or the cortex, while the lignification is much more pronounced than in subterranean organs. Since these latter are elements of the supportive system, they are undoubtedly due to the response to strains produced by gravity.

Conversely, in subterranean stems the fibrous tissues become little developed, and the lignification is feeble. Apart from the fact that roots frequently produce shoot-buds when they are exposed to light, of course many habitually develop buds underground, as plums, peaches, raspberry, *Anemone Japonica*, and *Neottia nidus-avis*, as M. Prillieux has shown, the adventitious roots of which develop a rhizome at their extremity, which continues to grow and increase in size for a year or more, until it is capable of developing a flowering stem. It would seem to be nourished by a fungus living symbiotically with it.[1]

Analogously with M. Mer's observations on the points of resemblance between aquatic stems and etiolated stems, M. Rauwenhoff has shown that the structure of etiolated plants is very degraded, and that the parenchymatous tissues, especially the cortex, takes an increased growth. Roots in darkness grow in exactly the same manner. The parenchymatous tissues of the root acquire great development, and the thickness of the cortex becomes much greater. He observes also that if there is a reduction of transpiration to which one can attribute this kind of turgescence of the parenchymatous tissues, the same cause ought to produce the same effect in a root as in a stem; and this is precisely what takes place.

[1] *De la Structure anatomique et du Mode de Végétation du Neottia nidus-avis. Ann. des Sci. Nat.*, Sér. 4, tom. v. p. 267, Pls. 17, 18.

Ordinary subterranean roots of herbaceous plants can assume, morphologically and physiologically at least, two well-marked differentiations. The one consists of fibrous roots of various forms, which are adapted as absorbents of water, mineral and other matters. The others are swollen, and mostly of a fleshy character, which act generally as reservoirs of nutriment; more rarely of water, as in some desert plants (*Erodium*, species). That both kinds of roots have been formed under the conditions of the environment, and have subsequently become hereditary characters, is borne out partly by analogy, and partly by the fact that, on the one hand, fibrous roots can be easily induced to form when a suitable inciting environment is provided, and on the other, that a fleshy character has been artificially produced by converting wild forms into hypertrophied culinary vegetables, as will be further described.

THE ORIGIN OF TUBEROUS ROOTS.—Many plants have fascicled roots, consisting of a mixture of fine fibrous water-absorbing roots and others of a thick and more or less fleshy nature, which act as reservoirs of organised food-materials. *Ranunculus Ficaria* will be a familiar example. This peculiarity is not at all uncommon in other species. Thus there are several in Malta which remain dormant for many months characterised by great heat and drought, and are provided with them. In these and other cases the appearance of tuberous roots is normal, constant, and can be recognised as a specific character.

In other cases they appear and disappear on the same bulb according to circumstances. They thus afford another instance to the many alluded to of a structure being formed in direct response to environmental conditions, but becoming a permanent character when those conditions are perpetuated. An interesting paper on this subject by M. Lucien Daniel shows how roots which are called *pseudorhizes dauciformes* can appear on several monocotyledonous bulbs under certain conditions, in which more nutritive materials are in the plant than it can utilise at the time. From his experiments the conclusion he arrived at is expressed as follows:—"Le système des pseùdorhizes dauciformes est un système compensateur transitoire qui se développe progressivement suivant les besoins de la plante, dès que, pour une cause quelconque interne ou externe, la nutrition générale se trouve entravée."[1]

THE ORIGIN OF ANNUAL AND BIENNIAL ROOTS.—Roots also differ in regard to duration; while fibrous roots may be perennial, though the short actually absorbing portion may soon cease to absorb, the others only last for one season.

The result is that this feature is often regarded as a specific character, as shown by the names *Bellis* or *Mercurialis perennis*, and *B.* or *M. annua*, *Œnothera biennis*, &c. Now with regard to biennials the question arises, how has the tap-root acquired its sufficiently enlarged size to enable a plant to live through one season on into the next?

Under cultivation biennial roots of course acquire a much larger size and more fleshy character than in the wild state; and although some of our "roots" are naturally biennials, like celery and parsnip, yet the carrot is naturally annual; and so is *Raphanus Raphanistrum*, which is at least *one* origin of the radish. On the other hand, beet-root, *Beta vulgaris*, is a perennial when wild, but appears to have the habit of a biennial when cultivated as mangold-wurzel.

In the case of these cultivated roots, the cause of their hypertrophied condition is of course artificial nutriment in addition to plenty of water; and when one compares annuals, with their slender tap-roots, with such biennials into which they have passed, one cannot but infer that the enormous

---

[1] *Rev. Gén. de Bot.*, vol. iii. p. 458.

difference has arisen by the influences of the external environment; that is, hypertrophy is an acquired character, which has become hereditary, for they are all now propagated by seed.

But in addition, we are familiar with the fact that the annual, biennial, and perennial conditions are extremely unstable. Not only is many a plant variable in nature, and therefore recorded in systematic works as "annual or biennial," "biennial or perennial;" but we know that climatal conditions change many plants, as I have had already more than one occasion to show. Thus annuals in low latitudes and on plains may become perennials at high latitudes and altitudes. On the other hand, increase of temperature tends to prolong growth, so that while the castor-oil is an annual in England, it forms a tall tree in Malta. This is analogous to the fact that deciduous shrubs and trees here sometimes become evergreen in the East, as the honeysuckle in Malta, while vines in Cairo scarcely shed their leaves in winter.

Whatever tends to check the reproductive system, or, on the other hand, to prolong the vegetative, may thus bring about an alteration in the periods of development of the various organs. Thus, mignonette can readily be converted into a small perennial tree by suppressing the flower-buds till it has attained a woody trunk and a considerable height; while it spontaneously becomes perennial in Tasmania.

All these facts are of course well known, but the point I wish to urge is, that when an annual has been converted into a biennial, *then* this "habit" may become hereditary, just as much as a hypertrophied condition of the root. That is to say, while the power to become hypertrophied is common to all roots as far as we know, *the predisposition* to store up nourishment becomes established and hereditary.

Now, as we can artificially *make* a plant acquire this pre-disposition, we are thereby justified in concluding that plants naturally constituted with fleshy roots have acquired this same peculiarity in some analogous manner, which is now hereditary. Hence we may safely conclude that it was the environment which established the biennial root of *Œnothera*, the adventitiously swollen roots of peonies and dahlias, and of some *Umbelliferæ*, as well as the "root-tubers" of aconite and terrestrial orchids. All these are traceable to some external cause which induced *storage* instead of *flowering*.

EXPERIMENTAL ILLUSTRATIONS OF THE ORIGIN OF CULTIVATED ROOTS.—I will now give two or three cases to illustrate and substantiate the preceding remarks.

M. Vilmorin's experiments in raising carrots illustrate both the change of duration from annual to biennial, and the hereditary predisposition to hypertrophy; for the carrot, or *Daucus Carota*, is naturally an annual and slender rooted, but the garden carrot produced from it is a biennial and rapidly grows to a relatively large size.

Now the first important requirement is that the flowering process should be delayed, so that the vegetative energy may be spent in enlarging the root instead of flowering—in fact, that the plant should become a biennial. In order to secure this end, M. Vilmorin noticed that the seeds showed very different rates of germination; some sprang up at once, others later, and indeed all through the summer. Amongst the tardy plants several never flowered the first season. These roots were selected and re-planted in the following spring. In the summer they bore seed, which was re-sown in 1835. Of this second generation, the proportion of plants which flowered was much less than in the first season, and about fifteen had fairly good roots. In 1837 the third generation showed a very appreciable amelioration, several being very large and fleshy. Only one-tenth now flowered in that year. In 1839 he raised the fourth generation. The quality was again improved, and scarcely any flowered.

Hence a garden biennial had been raised from a wild annual in four generations, solely by selecting the originally late germinating seedlings.

As another illustration I would refer to M. Carrière's experiments ;[1] for he raised both the long and short or turnip-rooted varieties from the same batch of seed from the wild *Raphanus Raphanistrum,* by growing them in a light and stiff soil respectively. He thus describes his experiment :—

"Pour donner à notre expérience, poursuivie pendant cinq années consécutives, une certitude plus grande, et la revêtir d'un cachet plus fort de véracité, nous avons expérimenté concurremment dans deux conditions différentes—à Paris, dans le sol léger et sec des pépinières du Muséum, et à la campagne dans un terrain plus consistant, dans une terre argilo-calcaire, *forte* comme l'on dit. Dans ces deux conditions, les résultats ont été ce qu'ils devaient être—*analogues,* mais *non identiques.* A Paris, la forme longue dominait ; c'était même à peu près la seule. A la campagne, c'était le contraire. De plus, tandis qu'à Paris nous n'obtenions que des racines blanches ou roses, à la campagne nous récoltions en outre des racines violettes et des racines brunes très foncées, presque noires, assez analogues au pavet dit d'*Alsace,* ainsi que d'autres *de toutes les couleurs et de toutes les formes possibles.*"

M. Carrière then gives comparative diagnoses of the wild and cultivated forms of the same plant. Of the roots he says, first of the wild plant—"*Racines* filiformes, sèches, fibreuses, uniformes, toujours blanches, dures, subligneuses, non mangeables."

[1] *Origine des Plantes domestiques, démontrée par la Culture du Radis sauvage.*

With regard to the new forms raised he says—" *Racines grosses*, parfois énormes de forme et de couleurs très variées, charnues ; chair blanche, parfois jaunâtre ou rosée, quelquefois violette, succulente et bonne à manger."

The author then figures several varieties of the ameliorated forms, as well as the wild original type for comparison.

In this experiment we have it shown that the two types of roots, the long and the turnip, were directly due to the two different characters of the soil ; that where the soil was loose and easily penetrable, the tap-root descended readily and produced the elongated root. When the medium offered more resistance, then the root became arrested and swelled laterally into the turbinate form. Then, by selecting from such as these, hereditary races have been established.

This result of M. Carrière's has been corroborated by M. Languet de Sivry, who found " that seeds of short-rooted carrot, when sown in a particular soil, in the alluvial deposits formed by a small river in France, yielded immediately, during the first generation, a number of long-rooted plants, either white or yellow, whose roots were very much larger than those of the parent plants. The seeds of the best or less deformed plants were selected, and sown in the same soil. The result was that in the second generation hardly any roots were found of the short type, and most were exactly similar to the common wild form."[1]

Pliny records a similar result as known in his day, for he says the Greeks have found how to obtain the " male " root—*i.e.*, the turnip form—from the " female " or long radish, by growing it in a cloggy soil. Both forms are, of course, now hereditary by seed.

The late Mr. James Buckman, Professor of Natural History at

[1] Experimental Evolution, by H. de Varigny, quoting from *Société Royale et Centrale d'Agriculture*, Sér. 2, vol. ii. 1846-7, p. 539.

the Royal College of Agriculture, Cirencester, carried out very similar experiments with carrots and parsnips, commencing in the year 1847.   In 1850 he had succeeded in raising three distinct types of parsnip from wild seed.   He describes them as follows : [1]—

1st. The round-topped long root, having a resemblance to the Guernsey parsnip (*Panais long* of the French).

2nd. The hollow-crowned long root, "Hollow-headed" of the gardeners (*Panais Lisbonais* type).

3rd. The short, thick, turnip-shaped root, "Turnip-rooted" of the gardeners (*Panais rond* form).

He finally continued his experiment only with the hollow-crowned form, which he called "The Student."

Messrs. Sutton & Sons, on receiving seed from Professor Buckman, raised it for commercial use in 1860, and are still issuing it as their "best variety" in 1895.

These three cases will suffice to prove that garden races of roots now hereditarily true can be easily raised from wild seed by cultivating them in a new medium.   The anatomical structure of the roots becomes profoundly affected, intense hypertrophy of the parenchymatous tissues and great succulency replacing the tough wiry character of the wild plants.

I made the following experiment to show how easily the tissues can be altered in an opposite direction, by preventing the plant from rooting at all.   Some radish seed of the long-rooted kind was sown in a tin tray of about half an inch of soil.   Under these circumstances the hypocotyl, which grew to about an inch in length, was erect *above* the soil, and not below it as usual.   The cotyledons soon perished, and the plumule formed a few small leaves.   The plants, however, lived for

---

[1] *Journ. Roy. Agric. Soc. of Eng.*, vol. xv. part 1, pp. 225–35, 1854.

several weeks. On examining the hypocotyl, I found that the arrest of growth was really due to the incapacity. of the plant to utilise the starch formed by the leaves; consequently the cortex and pith were densely laden with it. Secondly, as the hypocotyl was now in the air, supportive tissues were necessary and had to be formed to meet the strain of gravity. Sclerenchyma occurred on the inner side of the fibro-vascular bundles, and wood fibres were made, as well as a zone of collenchyma by the pericycle in addition.

This little experiment proved how readily the plant responds to its necessities, and forms special tissues at once to meet mechanical strains as required. Similarly we trace back the origin of the biennial state either to some accidental condition' in the soil, perhaps from being sown too deep, or possibly it might have been due to the seeds being poorly supplied with food materials. Whatever, however, may have been the *cause* which led to the delay in germination, the important point to observe is that the biennial state was easily fixed and made to° become hereditary.

Of course, when the tap-root of an annual becomes a fleshy biennial, marked changes take place in the anatomical structure of the root. "Disorganisation" might well describe the effects. There is a great increase in the parenchymatous elements of the cortex and medulla, the former being mainly due to a wonderful and increased activity in the pericycle, as may be well seen in the radish and beet root;[1] on the other hand, the vascular elements become degenerated. The original cells of the vessels become swollen and distorted and irregular in outline; the cylindrical tubes of the tracheæ are thus misshapen,

---

[1] In the radish the cortex of the hypocotyl soon splits, and the pericycle then forms the whole of the subsequent outer mass. In the beet-root the pericycle forms successive layers of cellular tissue and tracheids arranged in concentric circles.

producing what Mr. H. Spencer called "Absorbents," perhaps a better term than tracheids, as indicating their function of carrying the nourishment stored up in the root to the organs above-ground ; so that besides the generally enlarged size of the root being now hereditary, all these altered details of the anatomical structure become hereditary as well. With regard to the origin of the cultivated beet, I cannot do better than quote the following paragraph verbatim from the *Gardener's Chronicle* : [1]—

"The following is condensed from *Annales Agronomiques*. *Beta maritima,* which is indigenous on the borders of the Mediterranean, varies greatly according to its surroundings. It is biennial or perennial, never annual, and in habit also variable, the stems being often flat on the ground,[2] while on the cliffs of Istria, M. Freyn says that it grows in shrub-like form, with erect stems, bearing hardly any resemblance to our cultivated beet. But when grown inland, its habit changes, and in a few years annual and biennial plants have been produced quite similar to the cultivated beet, but readily reverting to their perennial nature. The result is very different when *Beta maritima* is grown in pots. The plants seed directly, are pyramidal in form, and bear ripe fruit early in September, being altogether much like the Istrian *B. vulgaris,* var. *maritima.* Clearly, then, *Beta maritima* and *B. vulgaris,* var. *maritima,* are not distinct species, but varieties of the same plant, differing only according to climatic and cultural conditions. When we remember that Chenopods in general, and cultivated beet-root in particular, are so variable, sometimes seeding in the first year, or, again, not flowering the second, or becoming shrubby and perennial as in California, it seems probable that *B. vulgaris,* our cultivated beet, is descended as

---

[1] Vol. xi. 3rd Series, 1892, p. 626.
[2] Compare this with other cases described *supra,* p. 101, *seq.*

directly from *B. maritima* as from *B. vulgaris*, var. *maritima*, two plants which are not specifically distinct. If the influence of the salt be also taken into account, it is evident that *B. maritima* is but a maritime form of *B. vulgaris*."

STEMS: INTERCHANGE BETWEEN STEMS AND ROOTS.—It has been seen above that stems are fundamentally the same thing as roots; and therefore it is not surprising to find that, as the latter can assume enlarged forms for retaining reserve food materials, so stems can do the same: and the question arises, how have tubers, rhizomes, &c., come into existence, and are now characteristic of genera and species of plants?

Underground stems, however, are not all tuberous. Many creep without being enlarged: and the further question arises, what has brought about this habit of elongating horizontally, as in *Carex arenaria*, *Triticum junceum*, &c., instead of remaining short and swelling into tubers, as the potato?

We shall find that there are very good reasons for believing that these habits have primarily arisen through the plants' responsiveness to the nature of their subterranean environments respectively.

First let us notice that certain localities are characterised by having tuberous or other kinds of perennials in greater abundance than annuals, as, *e.g.*, arid regions like the Karoo of South Africa; rocky places, like Malta; Arctic regions, as Spitzbergen, which has no annuals at all; high Alpine regions, where species are perennials which are annuals at lower altitudes.

Contrasting the structures of perennial plants with annuals, the most obvious cause of the difference lies in the excess of vegetative vigour over the immediate requirements of the plant for growth and reproduction; so that more materials are assimilated than can be utilised in mere annual growth. This excess may be correlated with a temporary or even permanent arrest of the reproductive system, in consequence probably of

certain climatic and other conditions.   Thus, *e.g.*, we may
account for the frequency of the viviparous state among Alpine
grasses ; or, as in the case of *Ranunculus Ficaria*, this species
rarely bears ripe seed in England, but propagates itself ex-
tensively by "root tubers" at the base ; and, as M. Van
Tieghem has shown, the pollen is quite arrested when the
plants propagate by axillary aërial corms.   Indeed, I have
found plants growing in damp, shady places producing
no flowers at all, but an abundance of these structures,
which contain stored-up nutritive matter.   Hence it would
seem that we are justified in concluding that the excess or
diminution of vegetative energy is the measure of the production of storage tissue, and the consequent development of
tubers, &c.

But this display of vegetative energy is, in turn, dependent
solely upon climatic conditions ; so that, in considering the
means of their production, we are driven to the same conclusions as elsewhere—that all kinds of storage structures are
simply due to the responsive power of the plant, which adapts
itself to the exigencies of its existence under the environment
in which it finds itself.   When these structures are formed
repeatedly, they become hereditary features, *i.e.*, so long as the
environment remains more or less the same ; but if climatic
and other changes occur, then the habit may relax, and the
special character may be lost for a time or permanently.   Thus,
e.g., leeks have normally lost the bulb-forming habit of other
species of onions, which they have in the wild state ; but it
occasionally returns in cultivation.

Now, it has been seen above that the histological structure
of roots when growing abnormally in air approximates that of
aërial stems ; so, conversely, when normally aërial stems are
made to grow underground, the new structures approximate
those of subterranean roots.   Thus M. Costantin found in

experiments with brambles [1] that there was a development of the cortical parenchyma, and a reduction of liber fibres in the subterranean stem, which are due to the influence of the medium ; while the great development of the vascular cords of the tubercle and the lignification of the pith are independent. He adds that the absence of light is one of the most important causes of modifications, which are *immediate in all' its tissues ;* thus the epidermis is suberified, and a suberous layer arises at the periphery of the cortical tissue. The cortical parenchyma augments, the collenchyma disappears, the foldings of the cells of the endoderm are visible for a longer time, liber fibres are wanting, or but little developed, the libero-ligneous generative layer is less active, the fascicles of wood are less developed, and the lignification only produces itself with difficulty. The ratio of the thickness of the medulla to that of the cortex is smaller than in aërial stems. Lastly, starch can be formed and accumulates, especially in the subterranean part.

M. Costantin then gives a summary of the effects. This is repeated more fully elsewhere,[2] whence the following is taken.

1. The modifications are uniform. They can be more or less according to the species, and are not contradictory, but operate in the same way.

2. They affect all the tissues.

3. They are produced rapidly, in a few days, or a week or two may suffice.

He records specific details as follows :—

1. The epidermis is suberified.

---

[1] *Etude comparée des Tiges aériennes et souterraines des Dicotylédones.* *Ann. des Sci. Nat.,* Sér. 6, 1883, tom. xvi. p. 4.

[2] *Influence du Séjour sous le Sol sur la Structure anatomique des Tiges.* *Bull. de la Soc. Bot. de Fr.,* 1883, p. 230.

N

2. A suberous layer can be formed.

3. The cortex increases by the increase of the number and of the volume of the cells of which it is composed.

4. The collenchyma disappears.

5. Endodermic punctations remain a longer time visible than in aërial stems.

6. Liber fibres diminish or disappear.

7. The generative libero-ligneous layer is retarded in its development.

8. This last feature corresponds with the feeble development of the ligneous fascicles.

9. The development of the medulla, when it takes place, is weaker than that of the cortex.

10. Nutritive matters can be stored up in the parenchymatous tissues.

It may be observed that this last result is particularly significant, as it points to the *rationale* of all subterranean storage structures, as well as the use of "earthing up" of potatoes.

M. Chatin has also written upon the peculiar structure of rhizomes, and observes that the differences are so great between a rhizome and an aërial stem, that the former " is neither stem nor root." [1]

Rhizomes, while retaining the essential characters of the stem, yet show approximations in many ways to the structure of roots, as, *e.g.*, in the endoderm or protecting sheath. M. Mangin also calls attention to the features of those stems of endogens which produce roots, that they resemble roots in possessing a true endoderm, &c. [2]

---

[1] *Sur les Caractères anatomiques des Rhizomes. Bull. de la Soc. de Fr.*, 1858, tom. v. p. 39.

[2] *Origine et Insertion des Racines adventives. Ann. des Sci. Nat.*, Sér. 6, xiv. 1882, p. 216.

Dr. Vochting [1] studied experimentally the development of tubers, especially of the potato, and has thrown much light on the physiological history of these organs.

He proved that the influence of the surrounding circumstances profoundly affects the mode of sprouting of the potato tuber. If no water be present, the tubers produce in the light short thick green shoots, while those in the dark form long thin pale outgrowths.

To show how the tuber-forming power is not merely hereditary, but "constitutional" in the system, he made tubers to grow in the dark with a minimum supply of water, when new tubers were formed in the axils of the branches that arose. He also compelled potatoes to produce little axillary tubers among the leafy shoots in light, by carefully removing the tubers and stolons below the surface of the earth, and by permitting roots only to enter the soil.

That climate can powerfully affect the growth of the potato was witnessed by "D. T. F." [2] in 1887, a year remarkable for great heat and drought, and which he says will be known as one of "long-topped but short-tubered potatoes." Thus "Magnum Bonums" had stems six feet in length, but "nothing but a full crop of swollen underground stems, resembling a sort of monstrous couch-grass or roots of green ginger."

Now since Dr. Vochting attributes the formation of tubers to an abundant supply of water, "D. T. F.'s" conclusion that these abnormal creeping stems were due to drought seems to be feasible.

We have here, therefore, an apparent analogy with many naturally creeping stems. Taking into consideration the dis-

---

[1] "On the Development of Tubers." By Dr. H. Vochting. *Bibliotheca Botanica.* Heft iv. Cassel, 1887.

[2] *Gardener's Chronicle*, vol. ii. 1887, p. 586.

covery of M. Carrière, that long slender radishes were almost alone produced in a light soil, but short thick "turnip" forms in a strong or stiff soil, and, secondly, that branches when produced underground tend to partake of the nature of roots, and so presumably share the tendency to be more or less affected by gravity, the resultant of the two forces of upward and downward growth compelling them to grow horizontally, we seem to have the clue to the origin of the long colourless stems creeping horizontally in loose dry sand, as is the case with *Carex arenaria, Triticum junceum,* &c.

CONCLUSIONS.—The observations of the preceding botanists will be sufficient to prove that when normally aërial stems are made to grow underground, the new growth *at once* begins to assume the characters of normally subterranean stems, such as rhizomes, and that both are in many points comparable to roots. The conclusion, therefore, is justifiable that it is the aërial and subterranean environments which act directly upon the responsive power of the organ, which then develops the structure appropriate for each medium respectively. Lastly, if the conditions be perpetuated, then the structures become hereditary.

CHAPTER X

ORIGIN OF THE STRUCTURAL PECULIARITIES OF CLIMBING STEMS

PRELIMINARY OBSERVATIONS ON THE EFFECTS OF LIGHT AND GRAVITY UPON GROWTH.—The question has often been asked, but never answered—why, speaking generally, do stems grow upwards into the air and roots go downwards into the ground? We name the hypothetical influences respectively Apogeotropism and Geotropism. In the latter case, gravity seems to be the cause. Like Heliotropism, Hydrotropism, &c., these terms only indicate observed facts, but in no way do they explain the why and the wherefore of the phenomena they refer to.

If we examine the very simplest organism, such as a spore, consisting of a single cell, when it begins to germinate, we should find, as has been shown by M. Rosenvinge[1] in the *Fucaceæ*, and by Stahl with the spores of *Equisetum*, that the primary cell division is laid down approximately at right angles to the direction of incident light; and again, it has been demonstrated by Leitgeb[2] in the case of ferns, that the dorsi-ventrality of the prothallium and the development of rhizoids, as well as that of the antheridia and archegonia on

---

[1] *Influences des Agents extérieurs sur l'Organisation polaire et dorsi-ventrale des Plantes. Rev. Gén. de Bot.*, vol. i. pp. 53, 123, &c.

[2] *Zur Embryologie der Farner. Sitzungsber. d. Wiener Akad.*, tom. lxxvii. 1878. See also Sach's "Physiology of Plants," p. 524 seq.

the shaded side of that structure, are the outcome of relative degrees of light, and that their position on the shaded side is not due to gravity.[1] In the higher cryptogams, the embryo always begins by forming four cells, one at each end in the axis of the archegonium, and one at each side. This pro-embryo forms the rudimentary axis, but does not directly grow into the aërial leafy plant. The growing points of the stem and of the root arise from definite points in it respectively. If the prothallium of ferns may be regarded as representing an early condition of things, which lies horizontally on the ground and develops its archegonia on the shaded under surface, we may think we can see how light penetrating through the prothallium down to the archegonium might have determined one of the upper (innermost) cells to be the shoot-end, while the opposite one, nearly facing the orifice and the ground, was the root-end.[2]

In other of the higher cryptogams, and also in Gymnosperms, the relative arrangement is the same; the suspensors, as in *Selaginella, Pinus,* &c., always pointing towards the orifice of the archegonium, while the embryo is developed downwards within the interior tissues.

Thus Hofmeister says:—"All the vascular cryptogams in which the germination has been observed exhibit the same arrangement of the first four cells of the embryo. This arrangement exists in the *Rhizocarpeæ,* the *Equisetaceæ,* and in *Isoëtes;* and the position of the first cells of the rudiment of the germ-plant at the lower end of the suspensor of *Selaginella* is the same. In these cases the primary leafless axis is formed principally by the multiplication of the lowest

---

[1] Similarly Hofmeister says:—"It is evident that shade is favourable to the production of sexual organs as well as of roots."—*The Higher Cryptogamia,* pp. 192, 193.

[2] See "Outlines of Classification," &c., by Goebel, p. 205, fig. 153, A.

of the four cells; of that one, namely, which is turned away from the mouth of the archegonium."[1]

The shoot-end of the embryo is thus always at first away from, and the suspensor or root-end towards, the entrance to the archegonium;- so that one may generalise theoretically (in the absence of any proof to the contrary), and attribute these relative positions to hereditary influences, the primary cause of incident light having no longer much, or even any, immediate influence in determining the polarity of the embryo.

Regarding, therefore, the developments of embryos as a whole, including those of Angiosperms, in which the radicle, as a rule, always points towards the micropyle, we seem to see the line along which evolution has proceeded; and that the first positions taken up in cellular cryptogams foreshadowed the future arrangement of all other plants. That light may have originally determined the polarity, and that afterwards this should have become inherited, even in the total absence of light, is of course quite in keeping with many other phenomena in plants, as Dr. Vines has observed in the following passage.[2] Speaking of the periodicity in the circulation of water in plants, he says:—"It has doubtless been induced in plants by the daily variations of external conditions, perhaps more especially of illumination, which are involved in the alternation of day and night; but it has become so much a part of the nature of plants, that it is exhibited even when the conditions which originally induced it are not present, and it is transmitted from generation to generation."

[1] "The Higher Cryptogamia," p. 201. Later investigations have added further details, correcting some of Hofmeister's original researches. See, e.g., "Outlines of Classification," &c., by Goebel, Oxford, "Germination of Ferns," p. 205 ; that of *Equisetum*, p. 259.

[2] "Physiology of Plants,", p. 96. See also (Index, s.n.) H. Spencer's remarks on other hereditary acquired characters.

When, however, a seed germinates upon the ground and the embryo begins to grow, the first process is the protrusion of the radicle with the development of the primary root, upon which gravity at once acts, determining the vertical position downwards. The plumule subsequently develops itself, so that its terminal cells lengthen the axis upwards. This erect position has been thus primarily determined by gravity and light.

We must not forget that if we call the result of the influence of gravity by the words "positive geotropism," and distinguish it from the upward growth by attributing the latter to " negative geotropism," that gravity *per se* has no power to do anything but attract all matter in a direction perpendicular to the earth's surface according to well-known laws. Consequently, when a stem grows in the contrary direction to this force, apogeotropism (if the term can be used dynamically) may be taken to include, first, " phototropism ; " secondly, the *effort* which the axis is obliged to make in order to overcome the attraction to the earth. In other words, it must support its own weight. If it do not succeed, it will of course fall to the ground. As long as the shoot is young and mainly composed of cellular parenchyma, it does this by means of turgidity and elasticity ;[1] for as soon as water fails, the shoot becomes flaccid, and, as all can observe, falls down. Subsequently it puts on supportive tissues, such as woody fibre, bast fibre, sclerenchyma, collenchyma, &c., to gain the same end. Hence it is impossible to attribute *upward* growth in any direct way to the force of gravity itself. On the contrary, all growth upwards in a vertical line is in direct opposition to it, and requires a continual effort to overcome its influence. Gravity, therefore, would be better described as only indirectly in-

---

[1] See Sach's " Physiology of Plants," p. 217.

fluencing plant growth ; in that it is really a stimulus under which the plant develops its supportive tissues, light having been really the primary determining cause of the stem growing upwards. This power, however, has long since become fixed and hereditary ; so that if a cut shoot be suspended upside down, whether in the light or darkness, the apex will nevertheless turn up again.

An additional reason for doubting the influence of gravity as a cause of the upward growth of the stem is afforded by Knight's experiment of growing beans on a vertically rotating wheel. In this case the root-end always grew outwards and the shoot-end inwards, the axis of the plant lying along a radius. Now, as gravity was practically neutralised, the root grew in the same line and direction as the centrifugal force, which itself being also an accelerating force, then acted *like* gravity ; while the shoot-end grew in the opposite direction, in the same straight or radial line as the accelerating centripetal force. Each end of the plant was, therefore, subjected to what might' be called an accelerating " pulling " force. If the shoot-end happen to grow beyond the centre, the apex will turn back again, being " pulled back," so to say, by the centripetal force acting along the other half of the same diameter.

Comparing these effects with ordinary growth in the ground, gravity acts as an accelerating force " pulling " the root *downwards ;* but there is no mechanical or accelerating force acting *upwards* analogous to the centripetal force pulling the shoot-end inwards on the wheel. Light, however, now comes into play instead, and the plant grows upwards under its influence.

Yet another illustration. It often happens that *Ranunculus heterophyllus* will send up a shoot vertically out of the water into the air. As the submerged stem ordinarily lies—but buoyed up at a certain depth—under water, gravity is practically neutralised at its apex, since the stems have nearly the same specific gravity as the water itself. We may, therefore, ask the question—why should the extremity of a long shoot rise up into the air at all? I take it that here again light is the sole agent which stimulates the plant to cause it to rise up out of the water.

Another instance of a similar acquired habit, originally due to light, is that of ordinary horizontal dorsi-ventral leaves. If their upper surfaces be reversed in position when young and so fixed, they will make the most "determined effort" to right themselves as long as they are growing; as I have found by experiment.

Plants grow towards the sky, therefore, because the earth is illuminated from above; but a lateral source of light will cause deviation from the vertical direction, as every one knows, from plants growing in an ill-lighted room.

Plants may, however, be made to grow upside down. Thus Mohl describes some experiments made with germinating *Cruciferæ*, by which he found that the influence of light might cause their stems to grow in the same direction as that of gravity; for when he suspended them in a horizontal position in a blackened box closed on all sides, and at the top, but lighted from below by a mirror through the open lower end, the plants were then induced to develop their stems vertically downwards.[1]

THE RESISTANCE OF PLANTS TO MECHANICAL STRAINS.— Assuming the preceding observations to be an interpretation of the fact that stems usually grow upwards, *i.e.*, in opposition

---

[1] "The Vegetable Cell," p. 146. Mohl uses the expression "overcame the effect of gravity." This is obviously wrong; for gravity acted, not in opposition, but *coincidently* with the reflected light in this case. It would have been interesting to discover whether the supportive tissues, by which a stem normally "overcomes the effect of gravity," were more or less reduced in quantity by growing downwards.

to the force of gravity, they must obviously counteract this force or they will fall to the ground.

There is ample evidence to prove that the protoplasm of plants so far resembles that of animals that it responds to the influence of external mechanical forces, and strives to acquire and to sustain an equilibrium with them. The so-called supportive tissues are the results of this effort. It need hardly be observed that plants cannot do this suddenly, like a man using his muscles to prevent himself from falling if he have lost his balance; but the result is no less effective, though it be executed by the slow method of growth.

On the contrary, in submerged water-plants this effort is not required, and consequently the supportive tissues fail to appear; for such plants are of much the same specific gravity as water itself, and therefore miss the external stimulus of any strain to which they can respond.

Similarly, with large and massive cellular plants, as those of the *Cactaceæ* and thick-stemmed fungi, but little or no other strengthening material, such as woody tissue, is required.

Precisely analogous effects occur under degeneracy. Thus M. Costantin's experiments prove—as have been alluded to—that when normally aërial stems are grown underground, the supportive tissues become at once arrested.

Use and disuse are, therefore, quite as applicable to plants as to animals; for while the muscles on the arm of an athlete increase with effort and decrease with disuse, so do plants develop tissues which best enable them to meet the various strains to which they may be subjected; and on the other hand, such tissues are more or less arrested when no strains are present.

It is thus that we find projecting angles and columnar structures composed of collenchyma on the surface of herbaceous stems, as in the *Labialæ* and *Umbelliferæ*; pericycular sclerenchyma in the flower-stalks, as of Carnations, Ixias, &c., and huge buttresses to some foreign tropical forest trees.[1]

EXPERIMENTAL EVIDENCE.—That mechanical strains bring about these results is proved by the following experimental evidence., Professor W. Pfeffer[2] has lately described the results of R. Hegler's experiments, showing an increase of strength and development of the mechanical tissues of plants resulting from the application of artificial strains produced by weighted strings. Thus the hypocotyl of a seedling sunflower, which would have been ruptured by a weight of 160 grms., bore a weight of 250 grms. after having been subjected for two days to a strain of a weight of 150 grms. The weight was subsequently increased to 400 grms. without injury. Similarly *Phaseolus* seedlings became strengthened. Leaf-stalks of *Helleborus niger*, which broke with a weight of 400 grms., were able to resist one of 35 kils. after having been subjected to a strain for about five days.

The increase in strength is effected by a strengthening of the cell-walls, generally accompanied by a great increase in the collenchyma. Bast fibres already in existence are greatly strengthened, and they may be called, into existence where

---

[1] As I am now only concerned with climbing plants, it would be out of place to describe the mechanical systems of other plants. The reader, however, may be referred to Sach's "Physiology of Plants," p. 218, where he describes hollow endogenous stems, calling attention to the fact that the lignified strands, &c., are "distributed according to mechanical principles in the organs." It seems to me that there is a strict analogy between the strengthening structures in plants and in animals; in that Professor Haughton has shown in his lectures on the "Principle of Least Action" how the muscular arrangements and organs of motion in animals all follow this law; that is to say, whatever force be required, the machinery exactly meets the case. I would therefore venture to lay down the principle as universal in the living world, that the necessary structures in both kingdoms have been evolved in response to effort.

[2] *Ber. Verhandl. K. Sächs. Gesell. Wiss.*, v. (1892), p. 638.

they do not previously occur, as in the leaf-stalks of hellebore. The strengthening of the mechanical elements is accompanied by a retardation of the growth in length.

My own experiments corroborate the above, for I find, when young horse-chestnut leaves have a weight suspended to the petiole, after some weeks the curvature becomes hard and rigid, and cannot be reflexed. Again, retardation is seen when a strawberry runner or one of *Ranunculus repens* is made to grow vertically upwards; the supportive tissue increases, growth is arrested, and though roots appear through heredity, they cannot develop themselves. As another illustration, it will be observed that on a leafy branch of a tree which has opposite leaves, *e.g.*, *Pavia*, Sycamore, Walnut, or Horse-chestnut, the lowermost leaf of any pair which stand in a vertical plane has a petiole very much longer than that of the upper leaf, in order to bring the blade to the front; the angle between the petiole and branch is much more acute, while the thickening of the base or pulvinus is intensified. This involves a much thicker layer of collenchyma, and a different construction and arrangement of the fibro-vascular cords. The leverage being at a disadvantage, or of the "third kind," quite accounts for the extra thickening at the base. Thus, the petioles of four pairs of leaves situated in a vertical plane of a horse-chestnut tree weighed respectively as follows :— '

	Grms.		Grms.		Grms.
1. Lower leaf,	13.00	Upper,	7.15	Difference,	5.85
2. „ „	11.35	„	5.55	„	5.80
3. „ „	7.20	„	3.90	„	3.30
4. „ „	9.35	„	3.80	„	5.55
Means ...	10.22	...	5.10	...	5.12

Hence the average weight of the petioles of the lower leaves was about double that of the upper; the difference being due to the extra development of tissues in the lower petioles in order to overcome the strain due to gravity.

APPLICATIONS TO CLIMBING STEMS.—This important principle of adaptation to strains, with the resulting alterations in the supportive and strengthening tissues, applies especially to climbing plants; for while, on the one hand, the main stem, which is no longer self-supporting, in a certain sense *degenerates*, to be further explained, by atrophy or "disuse," the parts or organs which have to sustain any weight or strain undergo changes by hypertrophy and become much thickened, &c.; hence arises the fact that so many stem-climbers are remarkable for their anomalous structures. The fact that woody climbers generally possess anomalous features would seem to point to some correlations with their habit of growth. M. Van Tieghem and M. Hérail,[1] however, do not recognise any causal relationship between these curious structures and the climbing propensity, although the former writer admits the coincidence to be frequent, for three reasons: (1) in some climbers the wood is normal; (2) similar anomalies occur in plants which do not climb at all; and (3) the anomaly affects the roots as well as the stems.

In reply I would observe: (1.) That some climbers with normal wood are exceptional proves no more than that in their case they have not yet been required to change, as the normal structure can avail for them. (2.) There are two replies to the second objection: (i.) That similar anomalies occur in other plants does not dispose of the suggestion of their being of special use to climbers, as each species must be judged and interpreted on its own merits; as, *e.g.*, has been already shown in the case of desert plants.[2] One would be rash to say that

---

[1] *Recherches sur l'Anatomie comparée de la Tige des Dicotylédones.* Ann. des Sci. Nat., Sér. 6, tom. xx. p. 203, 1885.

[2] *Supra*, p. 73.

there was but one cause for producing similar anomalous structures. (ii.) We can never disprove the hypothesis that, although certain plants are not climbers now, they may not have descended from such, and have retained an anomalous structure. Climbers are well known sometimes to lose their habit, or at least retain it in abeyance, and then to reacquire it, as in the familiar instance of dwarf French beans.[1] To give a remarkable instance, no one would à priori expect that a large shrub with a considerable trunk and branches, growing to a height of fifteen or more feet, could climb. *Hiptage Madablota*, however, growing in gardens in Cairo, often sends out one or more slender shoots, which twine around neighbouring trees or bamboos to a height of ten feet or so. It belongs to the order *Malpighiaceæ*, and therefore may be presumed to have retained a climbing habit.

As an interesting instance of plants becoming "sarmentous" elsewhere, M. Warming observes of such :—" Les parties boisées des Campos ou Cerrados sont à peu près dépourvues de lianes et de plantes épiphytes ; on y rencontre rarement une *Broméliacée* ou un *Ficus*, échappé sans doute de la zone des forêts. . . . Il n'existe pas de lianes dans les Campos, mais, phénomène digne de remarque, on observe une tendance vers le type sarmenteux chez certaines espèces appartenant à des genres qui fournissent des lianes dans la zone des forêts. Leurs rameaux longs de 2 à 3 m., trop faibles pour demeurer dressés, retombent en arcades. Le genre *Serjania* est de cette catégorie ; il est représenté dans les forêts par 18 espèces, ayant toutes les caractères de lianes, et dans les Campos par le *S. erecta*, dont le nom indique suffisamment le port. De même, le genre *Bauhinia* compte dans les forêts des arbres et des lianes, tandis que ses quatre représentants dans les Campos ont le même port

---

[1] See also Darwin's "Climbing Plants," p. 42.

que le *S. erecta.* C'est le cas aussi pour plusieurs Malpighiacées ; quelques espèces même de *Tetrapteris* et d'*Heteropteris* ont la forme de lianes dans la forêt, et conservent le port érigé dans les Campos. Les Dilléniacées et les Hippocratéacées n'ont pour représentants dans les Campos que des sous-arbrisseaux, tandis que leurs espèces forestières sont des lianes. Il paraît probable, d'après tous ces faits concordants, que le *Serjania erecta* et les espèces de même port sont issues de lianes, qui, émigrées des forêts, se sont adaptées aux conditions du milieu que les Campos leur ont offertes."[1].

An analogous feature applies to *Convolvulaceæ* in the African deserts, where species of Convolvulus form dwarf stunted little bushes, with no climbing properties whatever.

(3.) That the anomalous structure of the stem of a climber should appear also in the root is only what might be anticipated, since a root of a tree can put on ligneous tissues like the stem, and develop rings of wood to supply a support to balance the weight of the trunk ; there is no *à priori* reason why a root may not assume the same features as the stem of a climber. Indeed, we might say *à fortiori* it would do so ; for the structure of lianas does approximate in certain ways (as in the increase in size and number of vessels accompanied by enfeebled wood fibres) to roots. Further, since the root of a tree has to be proportionally strong to fix it firmly according to its size, and as the wood is formed in the stem, so is it continued down into the roots. This formation of wood depends on the foliage ; and if the wood of the stem be anomalous, so too will probably be that of the root, for it would follow suit, as it is equally dependent upon the assimilative tissues above ground and on the supply of nutriment sent down to it.

[1] "Lagoa Santa (Brésil)," &c. *Rev. Gén. de Bot.,* v. p. 151.

M. Costantin[1] has described the results of his experiments of growing ordinary aërial stems underground, and shows how they at once begin to assume a likeness to roots in their histological structures. Thus, e.g., and à propos of the present subject, the liber and woody fibres or supporting tissues are greatly arrested, exhibiting an analogous procedure with climbing stems.

If a transverse section of our common Clematis Vitalba be compared with one of a root of an elm, it will be readily seen how close is the general resemblance between them; the medullary rays being larger in the former, is the principal difference.

Mr. H. Spencer[2] long ago drew attention to the fact that plants respond to "actual and potential" strains, which he explains as follows:—"Actual strains are those which the plant experiences in the course of its individual life. By potential strains I mean those which the form, attitude, and circumstances common to its kind involve, and which its inherited structure is adapted to meet. In plants with stems, petioles, and leaves, having tolerably constant attitudes, the increasing porosity of the tubes, and consequent deposit of dense tissue, . . . takes place at parts which have been habitually subject to such strains in ancestral individuals. But though in such plants the tendency to repeat that distribution of dense tissue caused by mechanical actions on past generations goes on irrespective of the mechanical actions to which the developing individual is subject, these direct actions, while they greatly aid the assumption of the typical structure, are the sole causes of those deviations in the relative thickenings

[1] Etude comparée des Tiges aériennes et souterraines des Dicotylédones. Ann. des Sci. Nat. Bot., Sér. 6, 1883, tom. xvi. p. 4.
[2] "On Circulation and the Formation of Wood in Plants," by H. Spencer. Trans. Linn. Soc., vol. xxv. p. 405, 1866.

of parts which distinguish the individual from others of its kind. And then, in certain irregularly growing plants, such as Cactuses and Euphorbias [and I would add some woody climbers], where the strains fall on parts that do not correspond in successive individuals, we distinctly trace a direct relation between the degrees of strain and the rates of these changes which result in dense tissue." He records Mr. Croucher's experiments at Kew, which *proved* that cactuses developed wood where subjected to artificial strains; but when they were tied up, *no formation of wood took place.*

This last remark requires a comment, because the tying up may involve one of two conditions. If it *relieve* the strain due to resisting gravity, there will be no effort required and no wood formed; but had it been tied so as to subject the growing organ to a new strain, wood would have been made to meet it. Thus, if a bough of a tree be tied back, it will, on an immediate release of the ligature, return to its former position at once; but if it be kept tied for a season or two in the new position, though it may be afterwards released, it will be found to retain the position *given* to it because it has been making tissues to resist the strain until it is overcome and the forces are in equilibrium.[1]   Now, when we examine

---

[1] Professor Huxley remarks in the "Life and Letters of Charles Darwin" (vol. ii. p. 189) that: "One half of Lamarck's arguments were obsolete in 1850, and the other half erroneous or defective, in virtue of omitting to deal with the various classes of evidence which had been brought to light since his time. Moreover, his one suggestion as to the cause of the gradual modification of species—effort excited by change of conditions— was, on the face of it, inapplicable to the whole vegetable world." The reader will perceive that Mr. Spencer distinctly controverts and disproves this last statement of Professor Huxley; and I would venture to add my conviction, based upon many observations and experiments, that there is an abundance of evidence to prove that living protoplasm of plants is always responsive to mechanical strains and builds up tissues to meet them; or conversely, if a plant be not subject to them, a corresponding

the anomalous tissues of lianas, we at once see that there is the obvious difference between such climbers and trees or shrubs, in the fact that the stems of the latter are self-supporting, while the stems of the climbers are not, or only partially so. They acquire, as a result of their habit of growth, certain features which are very obvious, such as great length and flexibility. The loops and festoons which form themselves must necessarily be subjected to various strains, partly from their own weight, partly from the oscillations due to the swaying of the branches of the trees upon which they are suspended, &c. These strains must be met, or they will snap asunder like over-stretched cords, and I take the many anomalies of structure to be various self-adaptations of these plants to put themselves into as perfect a state of equilibrium as possible, compatible with the vital activities carried on in their tissues.

Although M. Van Tieghem and M. Hérail do not think that there is sufficient evidence to enable one to trace a cause and effect between a climbing habit and an anomalous stem, the former observer records a fact which certainly seems to point the other way. He thus speaks of *Wistaria :*[1]—" Quand la Glycine (*Wistaria*) enroule sa tige autour d'un support, on voit au bout d'un certain temps, de part et d'autre de la région en contact avec le support, une assise du parenchyme libérien secondaire devenir génératrice et produire de chaque côté un arc libéroligneux normalement orienté, qui est tertiare. Ces deux arcs libéroligneux s'étendent plus tard du côté opposé au support et peuvent s'y réunir. Pendant ce temps, l'assise génératrice normale continue à fonctionner et à produire du liber et du bois secondaires."

arrest of structure is the direct consequence. "Use and disuse," I repeat, with their effects, are strictly parallel in both the animal and vegetable kingdoms.   •

[1] *Traité de Botanique,* vol. i. p. 828, 1891.

M. Leclerc du Sablon[1] has also, and more lately, given a careful description of the development of the anomalous structure in the stem of *Wistaria*, and shows, in the first place, that there are no anomalies in the short shoots which do not climb, no secondary developments occurring; secondly, that the secondary and tertiary formations are produced in the climbing shoots *when the stem is subjected to pressure;* thus corroborating M. Van Tieghem's earlier observation. His words are as follows:—"La première année, la structure est toujours normale; mais la seconde ou la troisième année, lorsque le contact entre la tige enroulée et le support est très étroit, on voit la couche génératrice surnuméraire se former suivant deux lignes en forme d'hélice de part et d'autre de la surface de contact. Ordinairement la pression exercée par le support sur la tige affaiblit l'activité de la couche génératrice normale tout le long de la surface de contact; il y a alors une sorte de compensation établie par l'apparition de la nouvelle couche génératrice. Le plus souvent, on voit donc sur une section transversale la couche génératrice normale continue et la couche surnuméraire limitée à deux arcs de part et d'autre de la région de contact avec le support."[2] Thirdly, the older stems, which do not climb, may still form secondary and tertiary woody growths, apparently from the "acquired habit," as Mr. Herbert Spencer has explained in the passage already quoted. M. Leclerc du Sablon thus writes:—

"Il faut remarquer que dans les tiges très âgées de Glycine qui ne sont pas enroulées, les anomalies de structure peuvent se présenter, et qu'une couche surnuméraire peut apparaître d'une façon d'ailleurs irrégulière et sans jamais former un anneau complet."[3]

Lianas have not been sufficiently studied in their native

[1] *Rev. Gén. de Bot.*, 1893, vol. v. p. 474.
[2] *Loc. cit.*, p. 477.   [3] *Loc. cit.*, p. 478.

countries to test the point sufficiently ; but if these practical experiences with *Wistaria* may be taken for what they are worth, coupled with the general fact that similar as well as other features are generally characteristic of climbing stems, then we may at least offer it as a "working hypothesis," that the peculiar structures of climbing stems *are* due to the efforts made by the· climbers to strengthen themselves so as to resist strains and tensions, by making them flexible and elastic, so as to best meet the forces to which they are subjected without suffering injuries.

The *process* is thus comparable with the acquirement of all other self-adaptations, in that these latter are the direct out-come of reactions to external forces, and are the best fitted to fulfil the functions of plant life under the circumstances.

The example of *Wistaria* seems to prove that the new cords or arcs of supportive tissue are *developed just where the strain is felt,* and where it is required to strengthen the stem.   The above statement of M. Van Tieghem reminded me of the fact that in America *Wistaria sinensis* is often grown as a standard tree, which Mr. Meehan of Germantown, Philadel-phia, informed me never sends out long annual shoots, as the plants trained along a wall are accustomed to do, sometimes to a length of upwards of 30 feet in one season.   Mr. Meehan kindly sent me, at my request, some shoots of the same size and growth from each kind of tree.   The results of a micro-scopical examination bore out my anticipations, in that the histological details proved to be very different in the two kinds, as will be seen from the following details of their structures respectively :—The diameter of the shoots was three-eighths of an inch.   In the case of the "tree" Wistaria, the diameter of the pith measured 65 divisions of the micrometer ; while that of the "trained" Wistaria had 95.   The breadth of the woody zone or xylem measured 35 in the tree, and only 15 in the trained; the number of vessels in the space between two radii at right angles was 30 in the tree and 40 in the trained; the diameter of the largest vessels was 3 in the tree and from $3\frac{1}{2}$ to 4 in the trained. The liber fibre was much increased in the trained form.

PECULIARITIES OF CLIMBING STEMS.—I will now consider the probable origin of the anomalous structures to be seen in climbing stems, and see if there be not reasons for considering them to have arisen from similar causes.

The peculiar characteristics, both morphological and histological, of the woody stems of climbing plants have long been known, and various types of structure are well recognised, corresponding more or less to the natural orders to which they belong.[1]

It will be unnecessary to describe in detail the many well-known forms of lianas, but only to allude to some varieties. Thus, there are the "cable"-like forms, consisting of several twisted strands, each being a longitudinal outgrowth on the circumference of the central main stem. These are characteristic of the *Malpighiaceæ*. The "ribbon"-like stem is seen in *Bauhinia* and allied genera, bulging on both sides alternately.[2] These resist lateral strains: the gain of strength in these stems is quite as obvious on mechanical principles as in

---

[1] The reader may be referred to the *Eléments de Botanique*, p. 232, of M. Duchartre, and M. Van Tieghem's *Traité de Botanique*, vol. i. p. 822, where good figures are given, and numerous authors are referred to; and especially *Recherches sur l'Anatomie comparée de la Tige des Dicotylédones*, par M. J. Hérail. *Ann. des Sci. Bot.*, Sér. 7, tom. ii. 1885, p. 203. In the following descriptions I have mainly relied on my own observations on the anatomical structures.

[2] See excellent figures by Duchartre, *op. cit.*, pp. 233, 235. Reference may be made to Jussieu's *Monogr. de la Famille des Malpighiées, Arch. du Mus.*, iii. 1843; Gaudechaud's *Recherches, &c.*, p. 184, and *Traité de Bot.*, by Ph. Van Tieghem, vol. i. p. 823.

an ordinary hempen cable or a steel strap. Several of the *Sapindaceæ* strengthen their stems by supernumerary and localised ribs of wood running up the cork.[1]

As methods of securing elasticity, abnormal developments of liber fibre or of cork occur, as in *Bignoniaceæ*, where the wood occurs in the form of four or more widely separated rays, the interstices being apparently libriform. This occurs also in some *Malpighiaceæ, Apocynaceæ, Olacineæ, Aristolochiaceæ,* &c. ; several of the *Menispermaceæ* have concentric zones of wood, and often cortical tissue, alternating for two or three years, but afterwards the stem becomes eccentric. A somewhat similar arrangement to that of the first year's growth of the preceding is found in *Gnetum*, where apparently liber fibres alternate with wood.

The presence of such elastic or flexible tissues as cork and liber, in exceptionally large quantities or abnormally distributed, will probably tend to furnish a means for meeting strains without allowing the stems to be injured by too great flexure or breakage.

A study of the histology bears out this surmise, that the stems of climbers are adapted to meet strains by their flexibility and to secure strength by other means than by lignified woody fibre, this latter being what might be called the "self-supporting" tissue, *par excellence,* as in timber trees. The differences are exactly analogous to those between the strength of a ship's cable and that of a wooden post.

The following is a brief summary of some of the most important characteristics :—

I. *External columns,* giving a cross-section the appearance of having projecting cortical processes. Examples of this may be seen in herbs such as *Galium, Clematis Vitalba,*

---

[1] See Duchartre, *op. cit.,* p. 240, figs. 87, 88.

Humulus Lupulus, *Centradenia grandiflora*, and species of *Bauhinia*, in which the processes become "wings." The wings or buttresses consist of local developments of libro-ligneous cords.

2. Cortex.—This may be very thick, as in *Stephanotis*, or as in *Aristolochia Sipho*, where it forms two zones, an outer collenchymatous, and an inner layer of large thin-walled paren-chymatous cells. The concentric alternating layers of wood and cortical tissue in the *Menispermaceæ* are due to periodic activity of a cortical generative layer, the true cambium being in abeyance.[1]

3. Pericycular structures.—The pericycle appears to be particularly active in making special tissues in certain climbing stems. Thus in *Clematis* it makes alternate layers of liber fibres and suber, which as continually exfoliate from the surface. In *Aristolochia* there is a broad zone, well defined exteriorly, but less so within, of strengthening tissue. This appears to closely resemble many endogenous stems. In a species of *Piper*, *Lonicera*, and *Stephanotis* there is a zone of fibres of several rows. The ribbon-like processes of *Bauhinia* are attributable to its agency. The "fibrous" bark of many climbers, as the Vine, Honeysuckle, *Wistaria*, &c., are due to the activity of the pericycle.

4. Xylem.—The feebleness of the wood fibres, both in quantity and in the structure of the individual elements, accompanied by numerous vessels of large calibre, together with broad medullary rays, are features of very general occur-rence. They might be regarded, perhaps, as the most char-acteristic of woody climbers. Collectively, they offer much less resistance to strains, in consequence of their increased flexibility, than a dense zone of wood, which is more liable to

---

[1] M. Leclerc du Sablon compares *Wistaria* with *Cocculus* and *Cissam-pelos. Op. cit.*, p. 479.

snap. Besides the advantage of elasticity in the presence
of large medullary rays, as, *e.g.*, in *Aristolochia, Clematis,
Bignonia,* &c., the large-sized vessels enable water to pass
readily to a great length, an absolutely necessary provision in
rapidly growing shoots.

M. Hérail observes that the mode of life of climbers involves a modification of two kinds in their histological structures; the first being the development of the conducting
tissues, the second the organisation of the mechanical tissues.
To these two might, I think, be added the protective tissues,
e.g., cork and liber fibres. With regard to the number and
size of the vessels, this author gives lists of climbing plants
and of allied non-climbing species, in order to show the
marked difference between the sizes of the vessels respectively. The following are a few selected cases :—

Clematis Vitalba	. 90	*C. recta*	. . .	. 50
Cobæa scandens	. 130	*Polemonium cæruleum*	.	60
Calystegia sepium	. 120	*Convolvulus tricolor* .	.	90
Tecoma radicans	. 130	*T. Capapensis* .	.	. 35
Aristolochia Sipho	. 200	*A. Clematitis* .	.	. 70
Galium aperine	. 50	*G. Mollugo*	. .	. 10

Solanum Dulcamara affords a good illustration of these
differences, as they are exhibited in one and the same shoot
according to age. Thus a one year's shoot contains a very
lax and torn pith, surrounded by a very thick-walled xylem
with small and scattered vessels, though more numerous and
larger at certain places in the zone. These one-year shoots
which carry the leaves and inflorescences, do not climb, but
stand out freely into the air and light. They readily snap
across when bent. They have also a small amount of liber
fibres of considerable length embedded in green parenchyma
and a hypodermal layer of incipient cork.

In a second year's growth the thick-walled wood fibres are much reduced in quantity, and the vessels are now larger and more numerous. In all later years the wood fibres are thin-walled and the vessels very large and numerous. In this plant the medullary rays are thin, and show no excess of development. The surface now puts on a considerable amount of cork. The older shoots, say of six years' growth, are highly flexible, in consequence of the enfeebled character of the xylem.

POSSIBLE AIDS TO STEM PRESSURE.—Besides affording means of greater elasticity and flexibility in climbing plants, the large medullary rays, and in some cases the increased cortical tissues, may, I think, aid considerably in producing stem pressure to assist the flow of water to great distances. It is well known that if the surface, i.e., the epidermis and hypodermic layer, be removed from a herbaceous stem or petiole, they contract, having been subjected to a longitudinal tension, while the internal column elongates, showing that the tissues which compose it are under a constant longitudinal pressure. If, therefore, the parenchymatous tissues be increased in quantity, as they are in the large medullary rays, so much the greater will this tension become when they are saturated with moisture, as may be seen to be the case in a cut section of the shoot of a growing hop-plant. It is also a familiar fact that if a ring of cortex be cut out of a growing stem, and be cut vertically, it cannot be replaced in position, because the turgid parenchyma of the pith and medullary rays tend to expand in every direction. This being so, we can well understand how the large vessels must be constantly subjected to a transverse squeeze, in consequence of the horizontal tensions of the superficial layers.[1]

---

[1] This is not the place to enter into a discussion of the very debatable subject of the flow of water in plants, but I cannot but think that physiologists do not, as a rule, give sufficient weight to Kraus's investigations (*La Tension du Tissu et ses Conséquences; Ann. des Sci. Nat. Bot.*, x. p.

In the *Wistaria*, for example, of which I have given dimensions, the pith in the growing stem of the trained plant has an area more than twice that of the shoot of the same diameter taken from the tree form.

We thus see, if this interpretation be correct, that the alteration in the tissues brought about by the stems being supported are the very ones which are also most conducive to the carrying water to very great distances.

I think, then, we may now begin to see somewhat of the causes and effects traceable in the adaptations of climbers. Starting with the fact that they are supported, the first result is a degeneracy in the xylem, which remains pliable by failing to become very much lignified. This allows the vessels to be increased in number and size. The strains and tensions to which the stems are subjected are now met by means of the elasticity of the liber, cork, &c., while the stems themselves assume various forms to meet these external mechanical forces. We thus find the twisted rope-like form consisting of several strands in genera of the *Malpighiaceæ;* the ribbon-form, repeatedly folded and bulging on alternate sides, forming a succession of arches in reversed order, as in *Bauhinia;* while in

70, 1869); for tensions must always be present, and as water accumulates in winter, and at nights in summer, when transpiration has ceased or is slack, so the tensions will increase until they are relieved by the renewal of transpiration in the morning. These tensions will account for the *vis a tergo* necessary to supply the water for that function.

In the note "On the Ascent of Sap" (*Ann. of Bot.,* viii. p. 468), Messrs. Dixon and Joly say:—"Strasburger's experiments have eliminated the direct action of living protoplasm from the problem of the ascent of sap, and have left only the tracheal tissue as an organised structure and the transpiration activity of the leaf wherein to seek an explanation of the phenomenon. . . . Whether the draught upon the sap established at the leaf be regarded as purely capillary or not, these experiments lead the authors to believe that it alone is quite adequate to effect the elevation by direct tension of the sap in all trees."

others longitudinal and strengthening ribs are superadded, as in *Caulotretus heterophyllus.*

The structure of these examples is so obviously in accordance with mechanical principles of strength, that the general conclusion seems inevitable, that both morphologically and histologically lianas have acquired their peculiar forms and structures by self-adaptation to external mechanical forces; so that, on the one hand, atrophy has followed as the result of being supported, especially in the deficiency and feeble character of the wood fibres; on the other, hypertrophy is the consequence of their being subjected to various tensions and strains, though we may not be able to trace the immediate cause of the development of each individual variety.

Since degeneracy is a mark of the xylem in climbers, as also of aquatic plants and of Endogens, it is perhaps not surprising to come across more or less identical features. Thus in *Piper* there are isolated cords in the medulla, and these cords are often quite destitute of cambium. In others it may be detected by the presence of rows of cells converging to a point where phloëm is situated. The belt of pericycular tissue below the cortex of *Aristolochia* is very like that of Endogens, and may be regarded as a third point of resemblance to that class, its use being to strengthen the stem when the xylem of itself fails to be sufficiently supportive. In some cases the stem is absolutely zoneless, the cords being all isolated.

These considerations lead one to conclude that anomalous stems have become what they are *in consequence* of climbing. That the habit was primarily induced by mechanical contact on circumnutation is most probable. The universal phenomenon of sensitiveness or irritability to external stimuli was then called into action, and the climbing habit resulted. Then followed the alterations in structure as a direct consequence of this acquired habit of life. Lastly, they are reproduced by heredity, even when the plant may have ceased to climb altogether. Why there should be so many different types of lianas it is not possible to say; but variety is a law of nature. We might just as well ask, why are there so many forms of leaves, flowers, and fruits? The possibilities of adaptation in nature are infinite, and I, for one, would not attempt to reply to this question, though I think the growth in response to the influence of strains is identically the same as what is called "use" of muscular and other energy in the animal kingdom, and would be a correct general reply to the question, why is the structure of the stems of woody climbers anomalous?

I have hitherto confined my attention to climbing stems or "twiners," but the alterations in the structure of tendrils and other organs *after* having become attached to a foreign body illustrate analogous features.

Thus Treub has shown how the hook of *Uncaria* thickens enormously after attachment. Darwin also illustrates the petioles of *Clematis, Solanum jasminoides*; &c.[1] In these and other cases it is presumable that the hooks and petioles "feel the strains" when called upon to support the plant, and that they respond accordingly; for there is never any attempt to thicken these organs *before*, or unless the mechanical grasp has been made.

Similarly with tendrils, as soon as their apices have caught hold of something, they thicken in diameter and become spirally coiled or otherwise twisted. The thickening is to be explained as above, namely, as the result of effort. The coiling is a mechanical necessity to meet the new strain imparted to the tendril itself by its own growth. Darwin shows this well in the case of Bryony.[2] The long thread-like tendril, by

---

[1] "Climbing Plants," p. 46 *seq.*   [2] *Op. cit.*, p. 165, fig. 13.

continuing to increase after contact, coils spirally; but if it were to do so only in one direction, the force imparted into it would tend to wrench it asunder. This, therefore, must be neutralised by a coiling in the reverse direction; so that the number of coils either way is always approximately equal.

M. Léon has endeavoured to discover the cause of the reverse coils. He writes as follows:—"J'ai cherché à voir comment se formaient ces spirales inverses. Ayant remarqué qu'elles ne se dessinaient bien que lorsque le sommet des vrilles était fixé à un support, je plaçai le sommet des vrilles de Macon et de Citrouille en contact avec des brindilles fixées en terre, et par une surveillance attentive je m'assure que l'enroulement inverse de deux spirales voisines était simultané. La vrille se courbe d'abord dans une partie de son étendue, et cette courbure tend à se prononcer, à se resserrer en un point en demi-cercle. Cet arc de cercle devient alors le centre d'un mouvement rotatoire très lent, mais qui insensiblement tord les deux côtés opposés à cet arc mobile et leur fait décrire à chacun une spirale, qui, bien que dérivant de la même impulsion, se dessine en sens inverse; le point d'application des parties opposées agissent aussi à gauche sur l'une, à droite sur l'autre.

"Je puis indiquer un moyen plus prompt de vérification du mouvement que je viens de décrire. C'est de tenir dans l'eau par ses deux extrémités une jeune vrille de Bryone, ou mieux, sa moitié longitudinale. On voit sur-le-champ se former par un seul mouvement les spirales inverses. Le point de ce changement de direction, qui se marque par un demi-anneau, m'a offert, examiné au microscope, des cellules plus grosses sur les côtés, dans le sens du plus grand diamètre, que vers le centre de la section transversale; dans les spires, au contraire, les plus grosses cellules paraissent se localiser vers le centre de la section. Mais l'ordonnance de cette inégalité n'est pas tou-

jours à ce point tranchée que le point de départ d'un changement de direction puisse être reconnu d'avance sur une vrille.
Ces changements de direction des spirales des vrilles, examinés
extérieurement, semblent dus à des inégalités par excès ou par
défaut dans la flexibilité des tissus.   Il suffit du moins de
varier l'épaisseur des sections faites sur des vrilles, qu'on
soumet à l'expérience de l'endosmose, pour faire naître artifi-
ciellement et à volonté ces changements de spires, qui se produisent aussi sur les lanières détachées des tiges." [1]

It is evident from the preceding that the coiling is the
direct outcome of the tensions to which the tendril is subjected by the inequalities of growth throughout its extent, and
the reversing of the coils is a mechanical necessity to avoid
breakage from any excessive strain.

Similarly in the genus *Ampelopsis*, the two species of which,
so commonly grown in this country, not only illustrate a
similar feature of response to strains in their tendrils, but
they show how a merely mechanical irritation brings about the
development of the adhesive "pads" in the one case, previous
to the increase of the thickness of the tendril due to the
response to tension, and that the effect has become hereditary
in the other; for while *A. hederacea* has no trace of this
adhesive structure before contact, in *A. Veitchii*, as well as
in *Haplophyllum* (*Bignoniaceæ*), it is partially developed in
anticipation of the contact, but it is only completed on touching the surface of the wall.   Similarly the aërial roots of ivy
often protrude even before contact. [2]

Besides coiling, as in the tendrils of bryony, passion-flower,
&c., or zigzag bendings as in *Ampelopsis*, there is another way

---

[1] *Recherches nouvelles sur la Cause du Mouvement spiral des Tiges volubiles,*
par M. I. Léon. *Bull. de la Soc. Bot. de Fr.*, 1858, 679.

[2] See " Origin of Floral Structures," chap. xvii. on " Sensitiveness and
Irritability of Plant Organs," where I have further discussed this subject.

of neutralising a strain in a cord-like structure, namely, by the axis twisting back upon itself. If a piece of string be fixed at one end, and be twisted for some time at the other in one direction, it will be found that when the string is slightly relaxed, it will first of all coil up in the opposite direction (right or left, as the end has been twisting to the left or right respectively), and then *coil upon itself.* A precisely similar twisting is sometimes met with in lianas. An example is well figured by M. Duchartre of the rope-like cord of a species of *Malpighiaceæ.*[1]

The above few instances will be quite sufficient to show that the principle is a general one, that wherever strains are felt, plants invariably make an effort to meet them, so as to reduce the external and internal forces to a state of equilibrium ; and that this is done partly by simply obeying mechanical laws, and partly by new histological growths.

A THEORETICAL ORIGIN OF CLIMBING PLANTS.—The questions naturally arise, why do some plants climb, and how has the property arisen ? One may imagine that certain plants, unable to compete with others, such as trees in a forest, or tall herbs growing thickly together, might get "drawn" through want of sufficient light, and then the sensitiveness to contact being awakened, they were induced to climb in response to the external irritation. The resulting effect would be a great stimulus to growth in length, until they finally attained to the light and air by reaching to the tops of the trees as lianas in the one case, and above the herbage in the other. To render this hypothesis probable, several facts are forthcoming. Thus, Wistarias, when grown as standard trees, as observed above, never put forth long branches ; but if trained against a wall, so that they have not to expend their energies in making a

---

[1] *Op. cit.,* p. 233, fig. 79.

trunk in order to be self-supporting, they will make shoots often thirty feet or more in length in a single season. This example shows that the last of the surmises mentioned above would be fulfilled, and we know sensitiveness to contact is present or absent according to varying conditions and usages of parts of plants. It would not be altogether unparalleled to find that these weak stems were more alive to respond to mechanical contact than thick stems well able to stand erect. For example, the dwarf French bean with a thick stem requires no support, but it often puts out a long slender shoot which twines. Again, the thick peduncle which supports a bunch of grapes is not at all sensitive at any time; but the thin tendril, which is only a modified form of the peduncle, is highly sensitive.

Hence, while further information is wanted as to the real origin of climbing plants, it is at least a reasonable hypothesis that some such conditions as have been suggested were the originating causes of a climbing habit.

After the last paragraph was written, the number of the *Revue, Générale de Botanique* for May 1893 came to hand,[1] in which Dr. Warming continues his paper, *Etude de Géographie Botanique*, in reference to Lagoa Santa, Brésil. He writes as follows :—"Les plantes volubiles et grimpantes doivent leur développement à l'ombre épaisse des forêts. L'évolution de ces plantes paraît s'expliquer de la manière suivante : la jeune plante, développée à l'ombre, est forcée de s'accroître en hauteur ; ses rameaux s'allongent et s'amincissent. Le premier degré d'évolution nous est présenté par les plantes qui s'appuient simplement sur les rameaux des arbrisseaux et des arbres ; ces plantes sarmenteuses sont nombreuses dans la flore de Lagoa Santa ; elles comprennent des Amarantacées, des Composées, des Borraginées, des Euphorbiacées, des Violacées, et même

---

[1] Tom. v. p. 213.

P

des Cypéracées. L'adaptation est plus nettement accusée dans les plantes rameuses dont les branches s'insèrent à angle droit sur l'axe ; grâce à cette particularité, elles reposent facilement sur d'autres branches : c'est ainsi que les choses se passent pour le *Chiococca brachiata*, le *Buddleia brachiata*, pour quelques *Strychnos* et *Hippocratea*. Puis viennent les plantes volubiles. La nutation de la tige peut être mise à profit. . . . A cette catégorie appartiennent un grand nombre d'espèces d'Apocynées, Dilléniacées, Borraginées, Dioscorées, Composées, le *Boussingaultia gracilis*, des Asclépiadées, Malpighiacées, et Euphorbiacées." [1]

Similarly Herr Fritz Müller comes to the following conclusions from a study of climbing branches in South Brazil: [2] "We can trace in the development of branch-climbers the following stages—

" 1. Plants supporting themselves only by their branches stretched out at right angles ; for example, *Chiococca*.

" 2. Plants clasping a support with their branches unmodified —*Securidaca (Hippocratea)*.

" 3. Plants climbing with the tendril-like ends of their branches—*Helinus*.

" 4. Plants with highly modified tendrils, which may be transformed again into branches.

" 5. Plants with tendrils used exclusively for climbing— *Strychnos, Caulotretus*."

In all these cases I would contend that we have ample evidence to justify the belief that they represent gradually increasing differentiations towards specialisation in the climbing organs, and have been brought about in every instance by

---

[1] *Rev. Gén. de Bot.*, tom. v. p. 213.

[2] " Notes on some Climbing Plants near Desterro, in South Brazil." By Herr Fritz Müller, in a letter to C. Darwin. *Journ. Linn. Soc. Bot.*, ix. p. 345.

the direct response of the protoplasm of the climbing plant to the mechanical irritations induced by the other supporting it. It only remains to be observed, that the morphological and histological characters, which differentiate the various genera or species, or even orders, in which climbing plants occur, have arisen by "definite variation," *i.e.*, in direct adaptation to the environment, and consequently "without the aid of Natural Selection."[1]

---

[1] Since this chapter was written, a very interesting and fuller account of the mechanical adaptations of climbing plants to strains has appeared than I have place for here. I would, therefore, refer the reader to "The Natural History of Plants," by Kerner and Oliver, p. 724, under the heading, "Resistance of Foliage-stems to Strain, Pressure, and Bending;" and especially to the figs. 177–180, illustrating the structure of girders, which is paralleled by the mechanical tissues of many stems, as stated in the text.

CHAPTER XI

ORIGIN OF THE FORMS AND STRUCTURE OF LEAVES

GENERAL OBSERVATIONS.—The peculiarities of leaves are generally grouped under some such headings as the following:—(1.) *Position,* i.e., whether the leaves be "radical" or "cauline." (2.) The *Arrangement* or *Phyllotaxis.* (3.) Their *Insertion,* i.e., whether they be petiolate or sessile, sheathing or not. (4.) *Stipulation,* including the origin, form, and structure of stipules. (5.) *Direction,* or the plane in which the leaf-surface lies. (6.) *Venation,* upon which is based (7.) the *Form,* and (8.) the *Composition* of leaves. (9.) *Duration,* i.e., whether they be deciduous or evergreen. In addition to the preceding might be added special peculiarities, *e.g.,* spinescence, tendrils, ascidia, &c. ; and lastly, rudimentary states of leaves.

Besides these morphological features there are the physiological movements of leaves in response to climatic environments, &c.[1]

Taking each of these features in order, it will be my object to show briefly how far we can trace coincidences between the external conditions and any of the above special features under consideration respectively, if one cannot always prove the existence of some direct cause and effect.

(1.) *Position.*—Leaves often grow in a rosette from the top of the shortened stem, and are then called "radical." That

---

[1] For a paper "On Vernation and the Methods of Development of Foliage," I refer the reader to *Journ. Linn. Soc. Bot.,* xxi. p. 624.

this is a mere result of the conditions of growth, which are in turn produced by the environment, is obvious. Thus species called *acaulis*, as *Carduus acaulis*, naturally develop elongated stems when they happen to grow in valleys instead of on exposed hill summits, and especially in a rich soil surrounded by other plants, as long grass, when the stem becomes "drawn."

. Experiments, however, abundantly prove that this habit is an acquired one. Thus it has already been observed how high Alpine plants are provided with short stems as compared with those of the same species growing at lower elevations. Conversely, M. Bonnier shows that when he grew plants from low altitudes at high elevations on mountains, the stems were all arrested.[1]

The biennial habit, the reader may be reminded, is another cause of a temporary arrest of the flowering stem. Thus the carrot is normally an annual, but by checking its growth by sowing the seed in the autumn, the garden form has become biennial, and its stem is thereby arrested for a season, the leaves remaining "radical."

Hence the radical or cauline position is simply a result of the environmental conditions, and can become interchangeable accordingly. Thus carrots which "bolt" in the first year, as gardeners express it, are simply reverting to their ancestral or "annual" condition.

(2.) *Phyllotaxis.*—Phyllotactical arrangements of leaves can be accounted for on general principles, but why each species has its own kind cannot be always stated. I would refer the reader [2]

---

[1] *Supra*, p. 99.

[2] "On the Variations of the Angular Divergences of the Leaves of Helianthus tuberosus." *Trans. Linn. Soc.*, vol. xxvi. p. 647; and "On the Origin of the Prevailing System of Phyllotaxis," *loc. cit.*, 2nd Series, vol. i. p. 37.

elsewhere for a full account of the origin of the prevailing system; but would on the present occasion only call attention to a few facts which bear more especially on the case of adaptation.

It is an obvious fact that when leaves are crowded, the higher fractions of the ordinary series represent them. Conversely, when internodes are long, the lower fractions will be generally found to be illustrated. But the length of the internodes is a feature largely dependent on external conditions.

More striking and special instances are presented by plants which show a marked contrast in phyllotaxis, accompanied by as marked a difference in the position of the boughs. Thus, the common laurel, when it sends up a shoot vertically, has pentastichous leaves (2/5); but when it grows out horizontally from the side of the same bush, the leaves are distichous (1/2). A similar difference occurs on the same plant of ivy, *Ficus repens*, &c., between the arrangement of the leaves on the climbing shoot (1/2), and on those growing freely (2/5). The distribution of the leaves, *i.e.*, the positions where they emerge from the axis, is therefore clearly determined for them by the accidental direction in which the shoot may happen to grow.

Hence we at once see why the distichous arrangement prevails, and has become a fixed hereditary character of many trees whose boughs spread out horizontally, as the hazel, lime, elm, beech, &c.

Sometimes the distichous arrangement is mimicked, as by the yew. The leaves on the upper and under side of a horizontally-growing shoot are twisted to each side, giving a pseudo-distichous appearance; whereas in the Irish or fastigiate yew, the normal spiral arrangement, in which the leaves spread in all directions, becomes restored; presumably reverting to an ancestral state.

When exogenous plants have opposite and decussate leaves, they merely represent the primitive condition, as seen in the opposition of the two cotyledons.

(3.) *Insertion.*—The difference between a strongly petiolate leaf and a shortly petiolate one, and therefore more or less amplexicaul or sheathing the stem, is a matter of greater or less differentiation. The sheathing base is a mark of arrest or degeneracy,[1] in that instead of one strong central fibrovascular cord, together with two or more entering the petiole symmetrically, a number of separate cords pass off giving rise to the arrangement characteristic of Endogens, *Ranunculus, Umbelliferæ,* &c.

The length of the petiole and its distinctiveness from the sheathing base depend upon the requirements for reaching the light. Thus, in a compact plant like a dwarf *Tropæolum* long petioles are thrust out in all directions, carrying their peltate blades at right angles to the incident light.[2] The use of the petioles is obvious; but a dock with long broad leaves spreads them out so that nearly the whole length is fully exposed to the light. A similar difference may be noticed between the sessile submerged leaves and the petiolate floating ones of *Ranunculus heterophyllus.*

When the petiole tends to become vaginate or sheathing, we may see an additional adaptation to acquire strength to support the blade. This occurs in *Cyperaceæ,* Grasses, and Palms. In the last-named plants the weight of the blade must in some cases be enormous, and the strain on the petiole prodigious. This strain is met by the basal part of the petiole completely sheathing the stem, while there is, in addition,

---

[1] This is fully discussed in my paper on "A Theoretical Origin of Endogens." *Journ. Linn. Soc. Bot.,* xxix. p. 485, 1893.

[2] Kerner's "Leaf Mosaics." (Nat. Hist. of Pl., i. p. 419 *seq.*) would seem to be simply the result of every leaf trying to get to the light.

a complete network of interlacing fibres strengthening the longitudinal ones.

In Palms, therefore, we see the value both of the sheathing base and the long petiole carrying the blade to a distance to reach the light.

A similar condition of things on a small scale may be seen in a field buttercup, *R. acris*, which has a very long petiole and a sheathing base. It is obvious that the greater the weight of the blade or distal end of the petiole, so much the stronger must be the union at the base. Besides this, the pulvinus, as in the, leaf of a horse-chestnut, is another adaptation, which increases in strength if the weight increases, as described in the chapter on Climbing Plants.[1]

The point to note, however, in all these observations is, that such adaptations are invariably the outcome of the responsiveness of the plants themselves. Having acquired these various structures, they become relatively fixed and hereditary, and can then be used as classificatory characters.

(4.) *Stipulation.*—Stipules arise as dependencies from the lateral fibro-vascular cords of petioles. Thus if a central one and two lateral cords issue out of the cauline cylinder and enter a petiole, the stipular cords branch off from the two lateral cords before these have left the cortex to enter the petiole. If the leaves be opposite, a "stipular zone" is formed within the cortex by a fibro-vascular cord connecting those of the opposite leaves. From this arises normally four stipular fibro-vascular cords which normally correspond with and enter four stipules. But, as is always the case when the possibility of multiplication occurs, more or less than four may arise. This is well seen in the members of the *Stellatæ* of *Rubiaceæ*. Thus, in *Galium cruciatum* there are only four "leaves" to the

---

[1] *Supra*, p. 205.

whorl. *G. saxatile* and *G. anglicum* have the right number, six; but in *G. uliginosum* there are eight.[1]

Now the question arises, why are some plants stipulate, others exstipulate? It may be impossible to answer this question completely at present; but a few general reflections may perhaps suggest a hint or two as to a probable cause.

The first thing one notices is, that there is often a *compensation* between the formation of stipules and leaves. Thus, in the garden pea, in which several leaflets are converted into tendrils, and in *Lathyrus Aphaca*, all of them, the stipules are proportionately enlarged and foliaceous.

There is an anticipatory difficulty attending any speculations about the origin of stipules, in that they are now often characteristic of whole families; e.g., *Leguminosæ*, *Rosaceæ*, *Rubiaceæ*, &c. They must in these cases have been developed early and simultaneously with the differentiation of the orders themselves, while the various forms of stipules *now* existing within the boundaries of the orders respectively have become subsequently differentiated. Thus, e.g., we see that the stipules of the pea are obviously protective during the young state of the buds within their axils, but foliaceous afterwards. In *Acacia*, in consequence of drought, they have become degenerated into spines, the petiole being phyllodinous in compensation for the loss of the leaflets.

The questions, therefore, are, what were the primary and original cause and use of stipules?

Sir J. Lubbock has collected a large number of cases of stipules recorded in works of systematic botany, and has come to the conclusion that the general use of stipules is bud-protective, as previously suggested by Aug.-Pyr. de Candolle

[1] As illustrations of arrest, the stipular zone is present in *Valeriana*, but there are no stipules. In *Spergula arvensis* there are stipules, but without a "zone" or a circular fibro-vascular cord at all.

in 1827. Assuming this to have been so, we want to proceed further, and inquire not only into their origin, but into their subsequent differentiations as well.

Looking at the methods by which Nature now protects the undeveloped leaves within buds, there are two which are by far the most numerous, viz., by stipules, e.g., lime, oak, elm, &c., and by petioles, e.g., horse-chestnut, ash, currant, &c. In both cases these organs are metamorphosed into bud-scales.

It would therefore seem that when the blade is arrested in autumn, at the close of the period of vegetative growth, there remains vigour enough to develop the petiole in many cases; and if this be also arrested, then the stipules can remain and take its place as bud-scales.

The development of bud-scales, therefore, is primarily due to the reduced and localised energy around the site of the bud.

As stipules may be characteristic of certain genera only, even when the majority of their allies in the same order are exstipulate, as, e.g., in Ranunculaceæ, which contains stipulate forms, as Caltha, &c., it would seem that there is nothing to prevent their being formed in any plant except the want of localised energy to develop them, as well as the external stimulus, whatever it may be, to call that energy into action, if it be latent.

The study of a few examples will be instructive, assuming that the most general and obvious function of stipules is protective. On tracing the order of emergence of stipular and foliar papillæ around the *punctum vegetationis* of a bud, though the latter of the two may at first be the larger (as in the lime and the leaflets of the laburnum), the former soon outstrip them; indeed, in the beech the stipules are from the very first much larger than the foliar papillæ; and when the stipules are adnate to the petiole (as in *Rubus*, *Cratægus*, *Prunus*, and *Laburnum*), they are the only part developed in forming the bud-scales.

We thus see how buds are formed in the autumn. The vegetative energy being brought to a close, the leaves become arrested, the stipules being the only structures capable of being formed. These are then converted into the brown scales of many of our ordinary trees.

If their function be solely protective, the outer ones at least soon fall off on the expansion of the bud in spring; the inner may grow and be temporarily protective, as in the case of the lime.[1] Or they may remain, but apparently useless, as in laburnum. They may, however, be persistent, become foliaceous, and then assume assimilative functions, as in the hawthorn, pea, &c.

In the blackthorn we see a different condition represented, for the stipules remain rudimentary, and the leaf is *always in advance of them* from the earliest stage, being rolled round the bud, which it completely envelops and protects.

Bud-scales are often provided with the additional protective instrument of hair. Its presence is another corroborative example of M. Mer's theory,[2] that this epidermal outgrowth is compensatory on the arrest of the organ on which it occurs. But, of course, the presence of hair as a non-conductor is of vital importance in protecting the delicate immature structures within from frost.

The general conclusion is, therefore, that the development of buds in autumn is simply the result of climatic conditions coupled with the slackening of vegetative energy.

Conversely, if the temperature remain comparatively high and the air moist, winter buds are delayed or not formed;

---

[1] See my paper on Vernation, &c. (*supra*, p. 228).
[2] *Supra*, p. 59.

while the vegetation, and sometimes even reproductive energy, is prolonged or recommenced.

(5.) *Direction.*—The most obvious direction which the majority of blades take is at right angles to incident light.[1] But this is only the optimum position in temperate climates. To avoid an excessive degree of heat or of cold, the surface is placed in as vertical a plane as possible. As this has, however, been discussed elsewhere, I need only refer the reader to what I have said.[2] The vertical position may, of course, be assumed from other causes, as in crowding, *e.g.*, of blades of grass, pinks, thrift, &c. In all cases, however, the positions taken up by leaves is a self-adaptation in response to the various external influences by which they are surrounded.

(6.) *Venation.*—I had occasion to say so much upon this subject in my paper on a "Theoretical Origin of Endogens,"[3] that I need not repeat my observations; only noticing that of the two primary types, palmate and pinnate, the former is the more primitive or else degraded form, the pinnate representing a more differentiated state. These two types of venation correspond with the more or less dissected simple leaves known as palmati-lobed, palmati-sect, and pinnati-lobed, pinnati-sect, respectively. Thence are obtained the two corresponding main types of compound leaves, the palmate and pinnate, to be described more fully in the next chapter.

[1] "On the Power possessed by Leaves of Placing themselves at Right Angles to the Direction of Incident Light," by Fr. Darwin. *Journ. Linn. Soc. Bot.,* xviii. p. 420.

[2] *Supra*, p. 228. See also Kerner and Oliver's "Natural History of Plants," p. 347 *seq.*

[3] *Journ. Linn. Soc. Bot.*, xxix. p. 485.

CHAPTER XII

THE FORM AND STRUCTURE OF LEAVES—(*continued*)

(7.) FORMS OF LEAVES.—The shapes of leaves are well-nigh innumerable, but there are certain well-defined types which are not peculiar to special families respectively, and consequently are not presumably attributable to hereditary affinities. Consequently, one turns to the environment to see if there be not coincidences between *form* and *habit*. Observations show that there are so many, that enough of such evidences is forthcoming to lead one to suspect the existence of a distinct cause and effect. In a few instances experiment has decided the point, and thereby verified the deduction; but in the majority of cases the presumptive evidence is of the other kind, viz., a very great number of coinciding correlations; which are, however, amply sufficient to maintain the belief that *form is a result of habit*.

The reader must not suppose that I shall make any attempt to account for all kinds of forms, but only those which appear to me to warrant the conclusion. The rest must wait till we know more about the habits of plants on the one hand, and the influences of the environment on the other.

i. *Linear or Grass-like Leaves.*—The epidermis of rye, maize, &c., has elongated rectilinear cells with stomata at regular intervals. Now the leaf of thrift (*Armeria vulgaris*) has just the same, while in carnations they only differ by being rather squarer.

In a meadow-grass taken at hazard (and the name unknown), I found the cells over the chlorophyll tissue to be lozenge-shaped with stomata regularly situated at the angles. This type is exactly imitated by ·the leaf of *Pasithea cœrulea*, a liliaceous genus with grass-like leaves. In both, the two epidermides are alike, and, as in carnations, the palisade tissue is also on both sides. Another feature is found in the common pink (*Dianthus plumarius*) which is not pronounced in carnations (*D. Caryophyllus*), viz.; a circle of large cortical cells (as seen in a transverse section) around the fibro-vascular cords. This abuts against the pericycular fibres on one side, and therefore represents the endoderm.

This is exactly like many grasses, as of the genus *Aristida* of African deserts; but in them this layer is filled with chlorophyll, while in the garden pink I find it is clear.

In *Hordeum maritimum* and *H. murinum* the endoderm is present with horseshoe-shaped thickenings on the inner sides of the cells. This form is reproduced exactly in the grass-like leaves of thrift.

The leaf of thrift remains sub-conduplicate, like that of many grasses in arid situations. The cells of the epidermis of the lower, that is, the exposed surface, are almost identical with those of maize, having long rectilinear walls with wavy margins and stomata at the narrow ends, but wanting the silicious film of the *Gramineæ*. This outer, *i.e.*, lower, surface is of course most exposed to light, and consequently has a dense palisadic layer of elongated cells. Sclerenchyma fibres occur at the outermost angle and at various places. The concealed, *i.e.*, upper, epidermis has its two halves almost in contact, with deep sinuosities between the cords. This resembles many grass-leaves, especially those of *Aristida*, &c., of the deserts, which become clothed with hairs or watery papillæ standing over the stomata, which lie in depressions.

In thrift, however, presumably a result of heredity, there are no stomata in this upper surface, but hair is present in a more or less rudimentary form, like short cones. The epidermis of this concealed surface is very "epithelioid," just as occurs in the flower stem of crocus, where it is concealed within the sheaths below the soil; or, again, as the upper adpressed surface of leaves of *Thuja*, &c. The chlorophyll tissue of this upper surface in thrift is a lax merenchyma and not palisadic. Hence these tissues are reversed in position, just as they are in *Thuja*.

There are other differences, which are due to heredity and are not adaptations. Thus the stomata have subsidiary cells on either side, while quadrate glands secrete lime-scales, very closely resembling those of *Reaumuria* and *Tamarix* of the Egyptian deserts, described above.[1]

Plantago lanceolata and *Lathyrus Nissolia*, which grows among grass, have more or less grass-like linear leaves, with an epidermis resembling that of the above-described forms.

P. Klausch investigated the nature of the linear grass-like leaves of certain species of *Bupleurum*, and came to the conclusion that their forms and structure were adaptations to the external conditions in which they grew. In many cases the epidermides of the two surfaces of the leaf are quite alike, the internal structure bearing a striking resemblance to those of Endogens.[2]

That the dimensions of leaves, as well as their thickness, are regulated by climatic conditions, has been well established by Mr. Scott Elliot[3] in his paper on the effect of exposure on the length and breadth of leaves. He shows that length

---

[1] *Supra*, p. 82.

[2] See *Journ. Roy. Mic. Soc.*, 1888, p. 608.

[3] "The Effect of Exposure on the Relative Length and Breadth of Leaves." *Journ. Linn. Soc.*, xxviii. p. 375, 1891.

increases in shade and moisture, and that the ratio of the length to the breadth is always less in exposed leaves than in shaded ones. We have, therefore, in this fact an immediate interpretation of both the form and the anatomy of the grass-like leaves of many plants which grow crowded, whether they be on the same plant or in tufts, like pinks and thrift; or isolated among grass, as *Lathyrus Nissolia ;* or socially, like . grasses. Conversely, we perceive the general interpretation of the many broad leaves of trees, as of Sycamore, Plane, &c. Breadth is increased by exposure, as many observers have noticed, but only to an optimum degree. In deserts, where the heat and drought and glare are intense, the opposite effect is produced ; for the leaves are smaller in summer than those which are produced during the rainy season, or in the culti-vated regions of the Nile, as already stated in the case of *Salvia lanigera*, for example.[1]

As an illustration, Mr. Scott Elliot gives a table to show the differences between the measurements of the lengths and breadths of the leaves of several species of grasses growing in shady places and in the most exposed and driest spots he could find respectively ; the "ratios," obtained by dividing the lengths by the breadths, vary from 4.5 to 32.4.

The author then draws the following conclusions :—" This (the drawn-out character) is an important point in systematic character, as a lanceolate, linear, or oval leaf simply arises from the different proportions between length and breadth. If, then, climate or exposure can, as I think I have shown, produce variations in this respect on which natural selection [2]

---

[1] *Supra*, p. 46.

[2] Mr. Scott Elliot here pays the usual tribute to Natural Selection ; but his explanation of the origin of these forms of leaves clearly proves (as Mr. Darwin himself showed) that *Natural Selection is not required at all*, inasmuch as each individual plant varies *definitely* in response to its own environment. See *supra*, p. 1 *seq.*

may afterwards begin to act, we can see how a new species may be formed.

"The difference between *Ranunculus reptans* and *R. Flammula*, for instance, is chiefly a difference in the leaf-ratio—the leaves are longer and narrower in the second form; and Ross has experimentally changed the one into the other by growing them under different conditions, and, so far as I can gather from his paper, his method consisted in increasing the amount of moisture." [1]

ii. The ericaceous type, as well as that of the evergreen and coriaceous leaves, are well marked. They are associated with a dry summer and a mild winter, and occur, for example, along the South of Europe, where the *bruyère* (*Erica arborea*), *Arbutus Unedo*, together with *Quercus Ilex*, and olive occur; so also in Japan, the shrubs of which, such as *Euonymus japonicus*, may be compared with the European species. Again, the type reappears on the Karoos of South Africa, the plants of which are characterised by having small leaves, much cuticularisation, and a want of spongy parenchyma, so that they can endure a long dry summer with much wind; and Mr. Elliott adds his belief that "these physical conditions have produced this form." [2]

Lastly, the heaths of South Africa are represented by the *Epacrideæ* and other "ericoidal" forms in Australia.

The leaves of the olive and evergreen oak, as compared with the thin, deciduous leaf of the English oak, well illustrate the peculiarities of the type in question.

A more northern temperate climate, with a greater annual rainfall, is associated with deciduous trees, as in England; a result of a most marked difference between summer and

---

[1] *Loc. cit.*, p. 383. Similarly *R. Flammula* raised from seed in a pot bore cordate leaves at first.

[2] *Supra*, p. 46.

winter.   Still farther north we reach the colder and drier regions, where we find the evergreen *Coniferæ* with acicular leaves.   These, in their anatomical details, once more recall the structure of the most southern and dry climates.

The tropics are noted for their hot dry and hot wet seasons. These furnish a third type of evergreen foliage.

The question arises, are these distinct types the actual result of the varying combination of elements which go to make up these respective climates?

The histological elements, I think, leave no doubt upon the matter; though we may not be able to explain the immediate action of each individual factor of the environment upon each individual element in the minuter structures.

Analogy also furnishes an answer of some weight.   Thus, *e.g.*, the presence of resinous matters, which, as A. de Candolle observed, favours the protection of the *Coniferæ* against excessive degrees of cold, is the effect of the dry climate in which they live; for, as Sir J. D. Hooker observed at Lamteng in Sikkim, Himalaya, that not only was the timber of certain species of pine inferior, but that they produced no quantity of resin, turpentine, or pitch; "which may perhaps be accounted for by the humidity of the climate." [1]

Conversely, wax and resin are not characteristic features of tropical palm-trees; but the exceptional *Ceroxylon andicola*, which grows at very elevated regions on the mountains of New Grenada, secretes an abundance of wax.

The immediate cause of the evergreen condition is a prolonged period of vegetative growth.   This is practically proved by genera or species of plants which are deciduous in England becoming evergreen farther south, as, *e.g.*, the honeysuckle

[1] Him. Journ. (Minerva ed., p. 318).. The trees named are *Larix Griffithi, Abies Webbiana, A. Brunoniana,* and *A. Smithiana.*

in the Riviera and at Malta, while the cherry is evergreen in India. Many other cases might be mentioned.

A coriaceous texture is not infrequently associated with a spinescent margin. The reader will recall the leaves of *Mahonia*, Holly, *Quercus Ilex* (especially the young foliage), *Culubogyne*, &c., as all having a "holly-like" leaf.

Since it has been proved that spinescent features of all sorts do result from drought, as in the deserts, but the coriaceous type is more characteristic of exposed dry localities of more temperate climates than that of the sub-tropical deserts, there would seem to be enough coincidence to amount to a considerable probability that this peculiarity has been due to a dry and exposed condition, but not of intense heat.

An interesting illustration of dimorphism in a coriaceous leaf may be inserted here, which Mr. E. Tidmarsh has communicated to me from Grahamstown. He writes as follows: —"I send you the foliage of two species of *Aralia*, which would certainly be regarded as four species had I not known the plants from cuttings. One is that of *A. Veitchii*, as grown in a pot, and also when planted out in rather poor soil. The leaf sent was, in fact, taken from a plant growing under glass in a poor soil." They were about four inches long and one-fifth of an inch wide. ·The accompanying larger leaves were from a plant of the same species planted out in a mass of fresh compost in a hot-house, in a moist atmosphere, and with a temperature ranging from 60° to 90°. These latter leaves were five inches long and one and three-quarters broad. Hence, while the former are linear, the latter are broadly lanceolate and tapering at the base. He also sent leaves of *A. reticulata*, which were upwards of two feet in length and six inches in breadth. "The plant which bore these leaves," he writes, "was ten feet high, planted in the open on the banks of a stream, but too far above the water to be benefited much by it. It was under willows, which to some extent protected the foliage from the frost of several degrees experienced at Grahamstown."

A somewhat analogous difference is noted by Dr. Warming in writing of the plants of Lagoa Santa.[1] Of the plants in the dry Campos he says :—"Certaines espèces ont des feuilles très réduites et quelques-unes sont aphylles; elles appartiennent à des familles très différentes. Chose digne de remarque, les espèces forestières portent, en moyenne, des feuilles plus grandes et surtout plus larges que les espèces de la même famille ou du même genre qui habitent les Campos."

iii. The type of foliage characteristic of *Thuja, Juniperus, Tamarix, Casuarina, Veronica lycopodioides,* &c., in which the leaf is reduced to a minute, partly sheathing rudiment, would seem to be due to the same conditions as those which have caused the acicular, but have prolonged the arrest to a further degree. It is well known that two forms of leaves often exist on the same plant of any of the above genera or species respectively; and it is regarded as indicating a difference in development, the sharply-pointed form representing the younger type, the adpressed semi-adherent rudiment, a subsequent type. This accords with my contention that it is simply a still further degree of arrest; and therefore, when the pointed form reappears, it is a slight reversion due to an accidentally increased degree of vigour by having more moisture.[2]

iv. The aloë-leaved type would seem to be the result of the linear leaf, typical of Endogens, growing in hot and arid districts, so that it has acquired its excessive thickness and rigidity by developing an enormous mass of water-storage

---

[1] *Op. cit. (supra,* p. 2), p. 156.
[2] See *supra,* p. 108.

tissue; this being the most characteristic internal feature of such leaves.[1]

v. Fleshy-leaved plants are characteristic of maritime and saline regions, as samphire and *Plantago maritima* of our shores; and several Chenopodiaceous plants in salt marshes, &c. Again, dry and stony or rocky ground is also favoured by the presence of others, as stonecrops, while *Zygophyllum* frequents the desert.

M. Lesage, as already stated, has proved that salts are the immediate cause of the succulency in the first-mentioned cases; and we may safely surmise that the adaptations to the dry and hot localities frequented by others is equally an outcome of their environment.[2] Hence the peculiar forms assumed by the leaves of such plants is entirely due to their environments.

vi. Water is a powerful means of affecting leaves and producing the prevailing typical forms. I have had occasion to say so much upon this head that I need only remind the reader of the dissected form of foliage found in the submerged leaves of widely dissimilar orders, *e.g., Ranunculus heterophyllus, Cabomba, Trapa, Œnanthe, Ceratophyllum, Myriophyllum,* &c., among Exogens; while the ribbon-like type is especially characteristic of Endogens, though found also in *Hippuris, Lobelia Dortmanna,* and approximately in *Callitriche,* &c.

On the other hand, the floating form is very much the same in both classes, as seen in *Ranunculus, Nymphœa, Cabomba, Limnanthemum* of Exogens, and in *Hydrocharis* and (rarely) in *Alisma* of Endogens; while the final type reached in Endogens is usually the hastate or sagittate, as in

[1] For further remarks on the theoretical origin of this type, see "Origin of Endogens," &c. *Journ. Linn. Soc. Bot.,* xxix. p. 518.

[2] See *supra,* pp. 50 and 131.

Sagittaria and *Richardia*, these forms being transitional in *Nymphœa*, *Victoria*, &c.[1]

vii. Lastly, the extremely degraded aquatic type, which may be called "Algoid," is characteristic of *Podostemaceœ*, but typically found in many marine Algæ, as *Delesseria*, &c.

This rapid survey of the forms of leaves will be quite enough to establish the contention that they are in all cases due to their environmental conditions, coupled, of course, with the self-adapting powers of protoplasm, without any aid from Natural Selection.

The reader will perceive how the same lines of argument hold good in this case as in all previous ones; so that as each subject was brought forward in turn, they all mutually strengthen each other, as the argument is identically the same in every case.

viii. *Composition.*—That compound leaves are derived from simple ones goes without saying. The innumerable transitional forms alone would prove this; as, *e.g.*, *Rubus*, *Potentilla reptans*, *Ampelopsis Veitchii*, *Negundo fraxinifolia*, and many others; and it would appear to be a safe inference that the advantage to the shrub or tree in having deeply-lobed or compound leaves is that light can be readily transmitted to a depth within the bush or tree; which could not be otherwise the case if all the outermost leaves overlapped one another and left no interspaces for light to reach the underlying ones.

The question before us is, however, how are compound leaves formed from simple ones? One must first ask how are lobed leaves produced from entire ones, because lobed and divided leaves represent the transitional stage before complete separation of the leaflets is acquired. Let us select

---

[1] For further details the reader is referred to a full discussion in the paper "On a Theoretical Origin of Endogens," *supra*, p. 245.

an example such as is furnished by a vigorous yearly shoot of the snowberry, in which the following facts may be noticed. The first formed leaves at the base, ·where energy is not yet vigorous, are small and entire; towards the middle of the shoot, where energy is most vigorous, the leaves are much larger but more or less lobed. At the close of the year's shoot, the leaves are again small, like the first formed, and entire. Similar differences may be seen on a vigorous shoot of holly, &c.

Now in making the shoot, two factors at least are obviously concerned : one is the vital energy expended in growth and development, the other is the materials wherewith to construct the leaves, or the degree of assimilative power coupled with such nutriment as the soil may supply. At the beginning and ending of the period of growth energy is relatively feeble, the materials being just sufficient to make the small leaves entire. For the middle period, when vigour is at a maximum, materials fall short of what is required to make the largest leaves complete; hence the parenchyma between the lateral veins is not formed sufficiently to fill up the whole of the spaces and so round off the margins.

As the above described feature is not accidental and occasional, but now always true, it has evidently become fixed and is hereditary.

Hence, if the above be the correct interpretation, the original cause of "lobing" is simply one of nutrition : and whatever degree it has attained, from the repand state of an oak-leaf to the pinnatisect or palmisect types of many plants, it is now fixed and hereditary. It would seem, however, to be often liable to change according to varying degrees of nutriment and assimilation; thus pinnate and bipinnate portions often occur on the same frond of a fern, the terminal portion being pinnate, while the central and more vigorous may be bipinnate. •Similarly in *Rubus fruticosus* and *R. idæus* the leaves adjoining the inflorescence are simple, vegetative energy coming to a close to give way to the reproductive; but elsewhere ternate and quinate leaves can be found. Various methods are adopted; thus, the lowest pair of leaflets in the blackberry are "separated from" the first pair of leaflets, which had originally themselves been derived from the terminal one: the order of the formation of the leaflets is therefore basipetal. In the raspberry, however, it may be noticed that the lowermost pair of the two pairs were the first formed; the upper pair being *also* derived from the terminal leaflet, but *subsequently* to the lowermost. The order is therefore basifugal.[1]

In *Dracontium pertusum* we see a permanently established peculiarity in the leaves having "gaps" and "slashes" which the plant as a rule does not appear to be able to fill up, the habit being now hereditary and characteristic.[2] It is, however, by no means absolute; for if the plant be highly nourished and can grow vigorously, few or no holes may be left at all. On the other hand, they increase in number and size in a poor soil. Again, as illustrations of anomalies arising from insufficient nutrition, M. Fr. Buchenan[3] has observed a hornbeam which at first bore very small and lobed leaves, but, by an amelioration of the nutritive conditions, developed by degrees leaves of the normal form and size. On the other hand, M. F. Hildebrandt[4] has also observed leaves of *Rhamnus*

---

[1] The reader will, of course, allow for the use of the above metaphorical expressions.

[2] See "Origin of Endogens," &c., p. 522, for a theoretical origin of the perforations.

[3] *Ueber einen Fall der Entstehung der eichenblätterigen Form der Hainbuche (Carpinus betulus, L.). Bot. Zeit.*, 1891, p. 98.

[4] *Ueber einige plötzliche Umänderungen an Pflanzen. Berichte der deutschen botan. Gesellschaft*, Bd. ix. Heft vii. p. 24.

Frangula, of the walnut, and of *Hepatica triloba* to become lobed, this condition prevailing for several years.

That impoverishment and a want of an active assimilative power are the immediate causes of this peculiarity is borne out by other instances. Thus, submerged leaves, as the reader has been already reminded, are always more degenerate in structure than floating or aërial leaves. Hence it is not surprising to find some Potamogetons occasionally, and *Ouvirandra fenestralis* to be always fenestrated. I would here observe how very similar effects can be produced abnormally when buds are exposed to an excessive chill just as they are expanding. This not infrequently occurs in our spring-timo. Thus in horse-chestnuts the young leaves may receive a check, so that when the leaves are subsequently developed, they are found to be perforated and more or less pinnatifid. This is, of course, merely an accidental occurrence and not permanent, but it indicates the lines upon which nature appears to work in establishing the hereditary character; of lobed, pinnate, and other sorts of divided and compound leaves.

Another abnormal variety of many herbs, shrubs, and trees is the "cut-leaved." This occurs on many plants, and would seem from analogy to have resulted from an accidental deficiency of nutriment, or at least a want of assimilative power; and although it is somewhat doubtful whether it can be transmitted by seed, it is in a *sense* hereditary, in so far as, when grafted on a normal tree—*e.g.*, in the case of the beech—it may transmit the cut-leaved peculiarity ever afterwards on that side of the tree[1] to which it was originally united. The horse-radish is another example of a casual variation. When this plant is cultivated in a rich soil, it

---

[1] *Production et Fixation des Variétés dans les Végétaux*, par E. A. Carrière, 1865, p. 46, figs. 5, 6.

bears large lanceolate and perfect leaves; but stray plants growing in waste ground or gravelly soil often bear deeply pinnatifid leaves of various forms. No permanent variety has been established, but it shows how such leaves are caused; and all analogy seems to prove that if the influence be permanently kept up, *then* the dissected form may become permanent; just as with *Ranunculus heterophyllus*, which, when grown as a terrestrial plant, cannot recover the "whole" leaves, but adapts the dissected form to an aërial existence; but the leaf with its filiform segments has undoubtedly arisen by having been submerged.

The dandelion is a plant excessively variable in the incision of its foliage, the leaves being irregular and more deeply incised in dry places, but far less so in marshy ground, when it takes the varietal name *palustre*. Sir J. D. Hooker associates four forms with the following conditions respectively :—*Taraxicum officinale*, cultivated ground; var. *T. erythospermum*, dry places; *T. lævigatum*, sandy places; *T. palustre*, moist moorlands. To this might perhaps be added *T. minimum*, rocky ground, Malta.[1]

We thus have here a series of phenomena parallel with the varying degrees of hairiness, succulency, lignification, cuticularisation, &c., in that while in some cases excessive degrees are only casual or accidental and temporary, and not to be trusted as hereditary, in other cases they can be propagated by grafts and not by seed; while, lastly, similar structures in other plants are quite characteristic and permanent, and can then be used as classificatory, being fixed and hereditary.

---

[1] The reader may be referred to a paper entitled *Recherches sur les Plantes à Piquants*, par M. A. Lothelier, *Rev. Gén. de Bot.*, 1893, and Pl. 18, 19, where several comparative forms of leaves are illustrated; *Centaurea, e.g.*, having a toothed leaf in a moist atmosphere, but a deeply pinnatisect one in a dry air (Pl. 19, figs. 7 and 8).

This is all exactly what one would expect; for whatever the cause may have been primarily, *if it be continually in action* the result tends to, and often does, become fixed and hereditary.. Thus, too, M. Carrière writes :—"Faisons aussi remarquer que les diverses combinaisons faites pour perpétuer les variétés, ou pour en obtenir de nouvelles, reposent sur cette loi générale que, dans la nature, tout tend à se reproduire et même à s'étendre ; que par conséquent les modifications peuvent non-seulement devenir héréditaires, mais qu'elles peuvent encore servir de moyen pour arriver à d'autres modifications, à étendre et à multiplier de plus en plus les séries typiques." [1]

ix. *Duration.*—We divide shrubs and trees into evergreens and deciduous, according to the duration of their foliage ; but this is well known not to be absolute. In many cases, as has been already pointed out, deciduous oaks, cherry, and many other plants become more or less evergreen in warmer and moister climates, wherever "growing" conditions are prolonged through the winter season. Thus an absence of sufficiently strongly marked climatic contrasts, with the constant presence of moisture, accounts for the presence of evergreens in tropical climates.

The existence of the well-marked and persistent characters of "evergreen" and "deciduous" is therefore primarily due to climatic causes. They have thus subsequently become fixed and hereditary.

In addition to these nine classes of the peculiarities of leaves, I mentioned that there were several other special ones, such as spinescence, tendrils, ascidia, &c. ; but as these have been more or less already alluded to (as in the chapters on Desert Plants, Climbing Plants, &c.), further remarks need not now be added, beyond repeating what has been so often said—

[1] *Op. cit.*, p. 9 (*supra*, p. 249).

that a careful study of each phenomenon always reveals the same fact, that the probabilities are very much more in favour of self-adaptation to the requirements of the environment in each case than is that of any indiscriminate variations, from which Natural Selection can pick out a chance individual more fitted to survive than the majority of unfitted individuals, which are supposed to arise and perish.

GENERAL CONCLUSION.—It would not avail anything to add extra chapters on other parallel lines of evidence, such as the origin of depauperised states, of parasitic and insectivorous plants, &c., materials for which I have at hand; for if a reader be not convinced of the truth of my contention with the amount of evidence herein brought forward, he would probably remain unconvinced, however much might be added. On the other hand, I trust that the majority, if not all of my readers, will accept the conclusion that the Origin of Species is due to the joint action alone of the two great factors of Evolution—*Variability* and *Environment*—without the aid of Natural Selection ; although we are, and are likely to remain, profoundly ignorant of the mysterious processes within the organism by which it is effected.

INDEX

Printed by BALLANTYNE, HANSON & Co.
Edinburgh and London